An Activity Planner Designed to Accompar

MW00609338

The

MIRACLE MORNING

for NETWORK MARKETERS

ACTION
90-DAY
★ PLAN ★

Hal Elrod • Pat Petrini

With Honorée Corder

The Miracle Morning For Network Marketers
90-Day Action Plan

This planner would not have been possible without the design expertise and creative input of Mary Helgesen Gabel of Gabel Graphics. Mary has been developing professional planners for over five years and as you can see, she's amazing at it! You can connect with Mary at GabelGraphics.com.

Disclaimer: The advice and strategies contained herein may not be suitable for every situation. This work is sold with the understanding that the author and publisher are not engaged in rendering legal, accounting, or other professional services. Neither the author nor the publisher shall be liable for damages arising herefrom. The fact that an organization or website is referred to in this work as a citation or a potential source of further information does not mean that the author or the publisher endorses the information that the organization or website may provide or recommendations it may make. Further, readers should be aware that Internet websites listed in this work may have changed or disappeared between when this work was written and when it is read.

Interior Design: Mary Helgesen Gabel, GabelGraphics.com

Dedication

The Miracle Morning for Network Marketers 90-Day Action Plan is dedicated to every brand-new networker out there. Remember, "normal" is easy, and it is everywhere. The path to freedom is paved with criticism and rejection. Embrace the pain! :)

—Pat Petrini

Bulk Discount Program

Our hope is that you find so much value in *The Miracle Morning for Network Marketers 90-Day Action Plan* that you make it a core tool for both new and experienced marketers on your team. To help with that, we have created a bulk discount program with pricing that drops significantly with increased order sizes. We want to make sure that it's easy and affordable for everyone on your team to have a copy.

For more information or to order, visit

www.TMMforNetworkMarketers.com/order

For questions, contact us at **support@TMMforNetworkMarketers.com**

How To Use This Book

The 90-Day Blitz Page

Blitz: Sudden, swift, overwhelming attack intended to win a quick victory.

The 90-Day Blitz provides for a focused 90-day push. It is a relatively short window of time that when executed correctly, can create significant momentum. The dates are left open so that you and your team can start your 90 days whenever you want. Begin with where you are and where you would like to be in 90 days. Then, fill in the blanks with your best approximation of what you need to accomplish each month in order to get there. If you aren't sure of what to shoot for, get with a more experience team member that can help you set some goals.

At the bottom of the page, fill out what your Miracle Morning™ looks like. The recommended S.A.V.E.R.S. are listed on the right, but remember, this is *your* Miracle Morning™ and it can include anything that is right for you.

> **Bonus Tip:** Plan your Miracle Morning™ routine down to the minute including small details such as brushing your teeth or drinking a glass of water. This will not only help you form your Miracle Morning™ habit, but it will help you avoid *decision fatigue* (Google it!).

"Plan Your Work, Then Work Your Plan" and "Where to Focus My Effort" Pages

These pages are where the fortune lies. Here, you will examine what your organization looks like at the beginning of the week, decide what you want it to look like by the end of the week, and then brainstorm specific strategies to make it happen.

On Sunday night, follow the instructions on the organization chart so that you have a visual representation of what your team looks like. Put stars in the blank spots that you are going to work on filling that week. Then, brainstorm as many specific activities as possible for the week that will help you fill in your desired blanks. (i.e. "Host a meeting for Samantha." or "Get Charlie signed up for the training program." or "Help Bethanne set up 3-way calls.")

> **Free Bonus #1:** Watch Pat Petrini's detailed training on how to use these pages at
>
> **www.TMMforNetworkMarketers.com/90DayPlan**

Calendar Pages

Now it is time to move the best ideas from your brainstorming session on to your calendar so that they are sure to get done! First, add your existing commitments to the calendar for the coming week. Then, in the upper left, list your top priorities for the week. These are the best specific activities from your brainstorming that are most likely to accomplish your goals for the week. The left-hand column gives you a place to list new people you plan to contact, people you need to follow up with, people you are training, etc.

Now plan out your Monday by scheduling time for the activities that you plan to accomplish that day putting that day's priorities at the top. Each evening, plan your next day's activities (or plan first thing in the morning).

Most importantly, once an activity is on the calendar, *do not let other activities take priority as your day goes along!*

At the bottom of each day are spaces to check off your Miracle Morning™ as well as the business-building activities that you spent time on that day:

> 1 = Your Miracle Morning
> 2 = Prospecting
> 3 = Presenting
> 4 = Following up
> 5 = Getting people started

This allows you to look back on your week to see how you spent your time at a quick glance

List Pages

Of course any 90-day blitz will be successful only with a list of people to talk with. To help you stay organized, we have included pages in the back that are perfect for keeping track of your prospects. The "Master List" is a place to brainstorm everybody you can think of. The "Active List" is for the people you are currently actively following up with. The "Drip List" is for people that have said "not now" but that you still want to keep in touch with in case anything changes. Be sure to add new people you meet over the weeks and months. Be creative in your brainstorming! If you prefer to keep your list on a spreadsheet where you can sort, make ongoing notes, etc., take advantage of Free Bonus #2.

Free Bonus #2: Get a free copy of Pat Petrini's Prospect Tracker Spreadsheet at

www.TMMforNetworkMarketers.com/90DayPlan

Those Little Corner Lines

The dashed lines in the upper corner are there to remind you to cut the corner off used pages so that you can always easily open to your current week.

Samples

The following five are filled out as examples to show you what yours might look like.

Here's to your success!

Sample Pages

The next five pages are examples of how you might use this planner.

If you're a visual learner, Pat has put together an exclusive training video on exactly how to use this planner. Check it out here:

www.TMMforNetworkMarketers.com/90DayPlan

90-Day Blitz from ___10/1___ to ___12/31___

Set My Goal—Where Am I Headed?

What's my current status: Date ___10/1___ Rank ___Director___ Volume ___$1,500___

Where am I'm going: Date ___12/31___ Rank ___Silver___ Volume ___$12,000___

Now break it into 3 chunks

				Projected	Actual
Month 1	Date _10/31_	Rank _Elite_	Volume _$3,000_		
Month 2	Date _11/30_	Rank _Premier_	Volume _$7,000_		
Month 3	Date _12/31_	Rank _Silver_	Volume _$12,000_		

My Miracle Morning™ Routine

5:45 am – Wake up!	**S**ilence
Drink a glass of water and brush teeth (2 min)	**A**ffirmation
Protein Shake (7 min)	**V**isualization
Dress (6 min)	**E**xercise
Run (15 min)	**R**eading
High-Intensity Workout (10 min)	**S**cribe (Journal)

Recover with glass of water and a lemon (5 min)

Affirmations (5 min)

Meditation (10 min)

Read (10 min)

Journal (5 min)

Tip: See Pat Petrini's full Miracle Morning routine at

www.patpetrini.com/miraclemorning

Plan Your Work
Then Work Your Plan

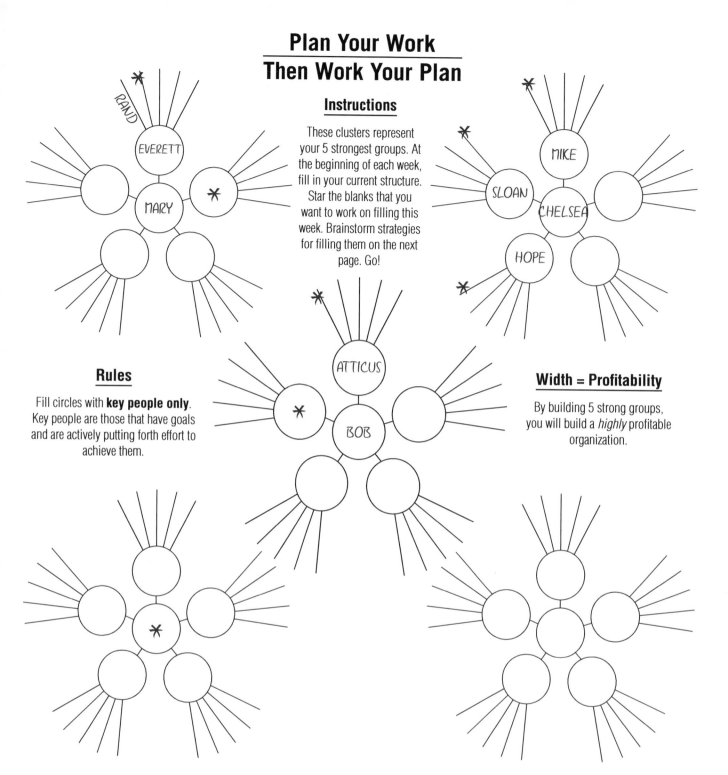

Instructions

These clusters represent your 5 strongest groups. At the beginning of each week, fill in your current structure. Star the blanks that you want to work on filling this week. Brainstorm strategies for filling them on the next page. Go!

Rules

Fill circles with **key people only**. Key people are those that have goals and are actively putting forth effort to achieve them.

Width = Profitability

By building 5 strong groups, you will build a *highly* profitable organization.

Depth = Stability

Work depth by helping 3 groups build 10 levels deep. By doing so, you will create a *highly* stable organization. At the beginning of each week, fill in the **key people** in the 3 groups that you want to focus on. Star the blanks that you want to work on filling this week. Brainstorm strategies for filling them on the next page. Go!

Key Group #1	Key Group #2	Key Group #3
1. CHELSEA	1. BOB	1. MARY
2. SLOAN	2. ATTICUS	2. EVERETT
3. ✱	3. ✱	3. RAND
4.	4.	4. ✱
5.	5.	5.
6.	6.	6.
7.	7.	7.
8.	8.	8.
9.	9.	9.
10.	10.	10.

Where to Focus My Efforts

Date __10/1/2016__   Current Rank ___Director___   Current Volume _$ 1,500_

Tasks

New Group:

☐ Make follow-up calls to all "active" prospects and see who's ready to go.

☐ Bring 3 personal guests to Thursday night's event.

☐ Invite 10 friends on social media to Wednesday's webinar.

☐ Create a Facebook group where I share valuable information related to my product category and invite people that might like to learn more to join the group.

☐ Try 5 new Facebook ad campaigns to my new landing page.

Mary's Group:

☐ Have brainstorming phone session with Mary (ASAP) on how we can get her second group going.

☐ Remember to ask Mary about Susan and Bill (prospects we met with previously). Can we follow up with them?

☐ Everett & Rand both need a "Getting Started" session. Can they both bring 3 people on Thursday?

☐ Can they both get 5 people on the webinar?

Chelsea's Group:

☐ Schedule a webinar specifically for Chelsea's group. Get Mike, Sloan and Hope all inviting to it.

☐ Schedule brainstorming call with Chelsea to see what else we can do.

☐ Did Sloan get a "Getting Started" session?

Bob's Group:

☐ Bob had 5 people at last week's meeting. What's the status on each of them?

☐ Are Bob and Atticus both coming to convention?

☐ Schedule brainstorming session with both Bob and Atticus on goals for this week.

Do conference call with entire team on the importance of using The Miracle Morning for Network Marketers 90-Day Action Plan! ;-)

WEEK FROM 10/3 to 10/9	MONDAY 3	TUESDAY 4	WEDNESDAY 5
THIS WEEK'S PRIORITIES	**TASKS**	**TASKS**	**TASKS**

THIS WEEK'S PRIORITIES	MONDAY TASKS	TUESDAY TASKS	WEDNESDAY TASKS
1 Brainstorm w/ Mary	1 Brainstorming sessions	1 Setting started session	1 Post on Social Media
2 Get Everett & Rand started	2 Follow-up calls	2 Invite for Thursday meeting	2 Team Webinar
3 Brainstorm w/ Chelsea	3 Grocery shopping	3 Back-to-school night	3 Follow-up calls
4 3 people to Thurs. meeting	4	4	4 Call Mom and Dad
5 10 people to Wed. webinar	5	5	5 Carl puts kids to bed
6 Brainstorm w/ Bob & Atticus	6	6	6
7 Webinar for Chelsea	7	7	7
8 Follow up with active prospects	8	8	8

Priorities/Contacts	Monday	Tuesday	Wednesday
	5:00	5:00	5:00
New Contacts:	5:30	5:30	5:30
Amy Lawson	6:00 My Miracle Morning	6:00 My Miracle Morning	6:00 My Miracle Morning
Bill Williams	6:30	6:30	6:30
Stephanie Broadhearst	7:00 Get kids off to school	7:00 Get kids off to school	7:00 Get kids off to school
Brad Smith	7:30	7:30	7:30
Jollene Marcus	8:00	8:00	8:00
	8:30	8:30	8:30
	9:00 Make followup calls	9:00	9:00
Followup calls:	9:30	9:30	9:30 Post to social media
Bruce Fine	10:00	10:00	10:00 about webinar
Pru Domingo	10:30	10:30 Getting started session	10:30
Betsy Holiday	11:00 Brainstorm with	11:00 for Everett and Rand	11:00 Call Mom and Dad
Zeke Williams	11:30 Bob & Atticus	11:30	11:30
	12:00p Brainstorm with	12:00p Lunch	12:00p Lunch
	12:30 Chelsea	12:30 Laundry	12:30
	1:00 Lunch	1:00	1:00 Plan for weekend
	1:30 Grocery shopping	1:30	1:30 camping trip
	2:00	2:00	2:00
	2:30	2:30	2:30
	3:00 Brainstorm with	3:00	3:00
	3:30 Mary	3:30	3:30
	4:00 Make dinner	4:00 Make dinner	4:00 Make dinner
	4:30	4:30	4:30
	5:00 Dinner	5:00 Dinner	5:00 Dinner
	5:30	5:30	5:30
	6:00 Make follow-up calls	6:00 Make invite calls for	6:00 Team Webinar
	6:30	6:30 Thurs. Mtg.	6:30
	7:00	7:00 Pick up baby sitter	7:00 Make follow-up calls
	7:30	7:30 Back-to-school night	7:30
	8:00 Put kids to bed	8:00	8:00
	8:30	8:30	8:30
	9:00	9:00	9:00
	9:30	9:30	9:30
	10:00	10:00	10:00
	10:30	10:30	10:30

> *Do or do not . . . there is no try.* —Yoda

TIME FOCUS KEY

1 = Your Miracle Morning
2 = Prospecting
3 = Presenting
4 = Following up
5 = Getting people started

TIME FOCUS:	1	2	3	4	5	1	2	3	4	5	1	2	3	4	5
✔ when completed:	✔	✔		✔		✔	✔			✔	✔		✔	✔	

THURSDAY 6	FRIDAY 7	SATURDAY 8	SUNDAY 9
TASKS	**TASKS**	**TASKS**	**TASKS**

#	Thursday	Friday	Saturday	Sunday
1	Opportunity Overview	Prospect for coffee	Family camping trip	Family camping trip
2	Text to confirm	presentations		Plan for next week
3	Carl makes dinner/puts	Pack for camping		
4	kids to bed			
5				
6				
7				
8				

Time	Thursday	Friday	Saturday	Sunday
5:00				
5:30				
6:00	My Miracle Morning	My Miracle Morning	My Miracle Morning	My Miracle Morning
6:30				
7:00	Get kids off to school			
7:30			Camping	Camping
8:00				
8:30				
9:00				
9:30				
10:00				
10:30		Make calls to invite to		
11:00		coffee presentations		
11:30				
12:00p	Lunch	Lunch		
12:30				
1:00	Send texts to confirm	Pack for camping		
1:30	who is coming tonight			
2:00				
2:30				
3:00				
3:30				
4:00				
4:30				
5:00	Dinner			
5:30		Dinner		
6:00				
6:30		Leave on trip		
7:00	Opportunity Overview			
7:30	@ Hilton			
8:00				
8:30				Plan for next week
9:00				
9:30				
10:00				
10:30				

	1	2	3	4	5
Thursday	✔	✔	✔		
Friday	✔	✔			
Saturday	✔				
Sunday	✔				

Your Turn

Now go! Here's to your success.

90-Day Blitz from _____ to _____

Set My Goal—Where Am I Headed?

What's my current status: Date _____   Rank _____   Volume _____

Where am I'm going: Date _____   Rank _____   Volume _____

Now break it into 3 chunks   *Projected*   *Actual*

Month 1   Date _____   Rank _____   Volume _____   _____

Month 2   Date _____   Rank _____   Volume _____   _____

Month 3   Date _____   Rank _____   Volume _____   _____

My Miracle Morning™ Routine

S ilence
A ffirmation
V isualization
E xercise
R eading
S cribe (Journal)

_____
_____
_____
_____
_____
_____
_____
_____
_____
_____
_____
_____
_____
_____
_____

Plan Your Work
Then Work Your Plan

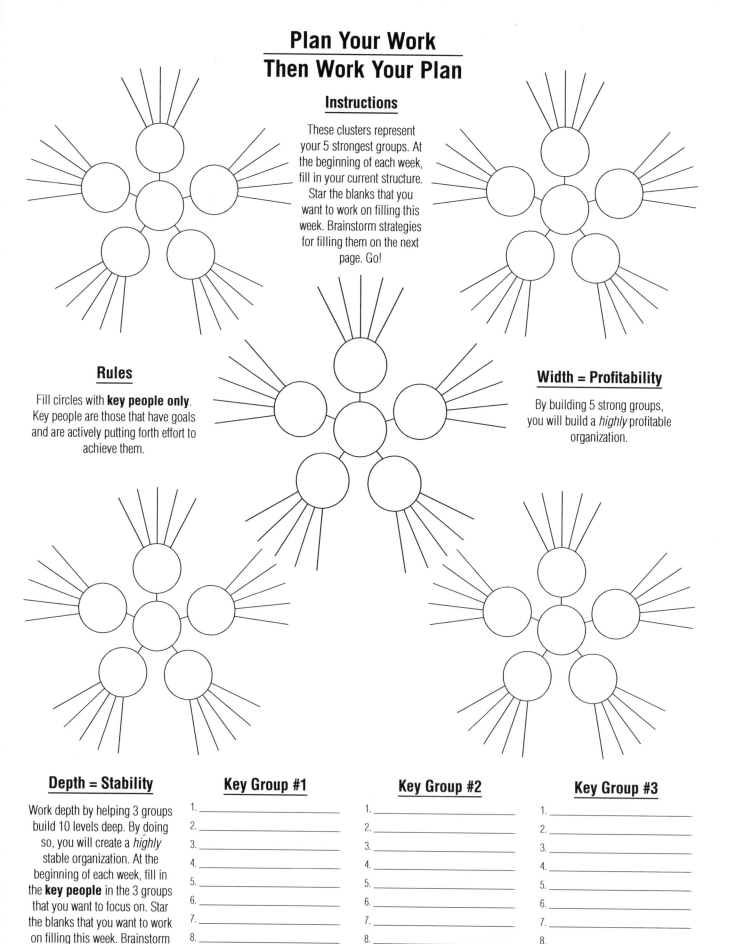

Instructions

These clusters represent your 5 strongest groups. At the beginning of each week, fill in your current structure. Star the blanks that you want to work on filling this week. Brainstorm strategies for filling them on the next page. Go!

Rules

Fill circles with **key people only**. Key people are those that have goals and are actively putting forth effort to achieve them.

Width = Profitability

By building 5 strong groups, you will build a *highly* profitable organization.

Depth = Stability

Work depth by helping 3 groups build 10 levels deep. By doing so, you will create a *highly* stable organization. At the beginning of each week, fill in the **key people** in the 3 groups that you want to focus on. Star the blanks that you want to work on filling this week. Brainstorm strategies for filling them on the next page. Go!

Key Group #1

1. _____
2. _____
3. _____
4. _____
5. _____
6. _____
7. _____
8. _____
9. _____
10. _____

Key Group #2

1. _____
2. _____
3. _____
4. _____
5. _____
6. _____
7. _____
8. _____
9. _____
10. _____

Key Group #3

1. _____
2. _____
3. _____
4. _____
5. _____
6. _____
7. _____
8. _____
9. _____
10. _____

Where to Focus My Efforts

Date _____ Current Rank _____ Current Volume $_____

Tasks

WEEK FROM	/ TO /	MONDAY		TUESDAY		WEDNESDAY	
THIS WEEK'S PRIORITIES		**TASKS**		**TASKS**		**TASKS**	
1		1		1		1	
2		2		2		2	
3		3		3		3	
4		4		4		4	
5		5		5		5	
6		6		6		6	
7		7		7		7	
8		8		8		8	
		5:00		5:00		5:00	
		5:30		5:30		5:30	
		6:00		6:00		6:00	
		6:30		6:30		6:30	
		7:00		7:00		7:00	
		7:30		7:30		7:30	
		8:00		8:00		8:00	
		8:30		8:30		8:30	
		9:00		9:00		9:00	
		9:30		9:30		9:30	
		10:00		10:00		10:00	
		10:30		10:30		10:30	
		11:00		11:00		11:00	
		11:30		11:30		11:30	
		12:00p		12:00p		12:00p	
		12:30		12:30		12:30	
		1:00		1:00		1:00	
		1:30		1:30		1:30	
		2:00		2:00		2:00	
		2:30		2:30		2:30	
		3:00		3:00		3:00	
		3:30		3:30		3:30	
		4:00		4:00		4:00	
		4:30		4:30		4:30	
		5:00		5:00		5:00	
		5:30		5:30		5:30	
		6:00		6:00		6:00	
		6:30		6:30		6:30	
		7:00		7:00		7:00	
		7:30		7:30		7:30	
		8:00		8:00		8:00	
		8:30		8:30		8:30	
		9:00		9:00		9:00	
		9:30		9:30		9:30	
		10:00		10:00		10:00	
		10:30		10:30		10:30	

Our deepest fear is not that we are inadequate. Our deepest fear is that we are powerful beyond measure.
— Marian Williams

TIME FOCUS KEY
1 = Your Miracle Morning
2 = Prospecting
3 = Presenting
4 = Following up
5 = Getting people started

TIME FOCUS:	1	2	3	4	5	1	2	3	4	5	1	2	3	4	5
✔ when completed:															

THURSDAY		FRIDAY		SATURDAY		SUNDAY	
TASKS		**TASKS**		**TASKS**		**TASKS**	
1		1		1		1	
2		2		2		2	
3		3		3		3	
4		4		4		4	
5		5		5		5	
6		6		6		6	
7		7		7		7	
8		8		8		8	
5:00		5:00		5:00		5:00	
5:30		5:30		5:30		5:30	
6:00		6:00		6:00		6:00	
6:30		6:30		6:30		6:30	
7:00		7:00		7:00		7:00	
7:30		7:30		7:30		7:30	
8:00		8:00		8:00		8:00	
8:30		8:30		8:30		8:30	
9:00		9:00		9:00		9:00	
9:30		9:30		9:30		9:30	
10:00		10:00		10:00		10:00	
10:30		10:30		10:30		10:30	
11:00		11:00		11:00		11:00	
11:30		11:30		11:30		11:30	
12:00p		12:00p		12:00p		12:00p	
12:30		12:30		12:30		12:30	
1:00		1:00		1:00		1:00	
1:30		1:30		1:30		1:30	
2:00		2:00		2:00		2:00	
2:30		2:30		2:30		2:30	
3:00		3:00		3:00		3:00	
3:30		3:30		3:30		3:30	
4:00		4:00		4:00		4:00	
4:30		4:30		4:30		4:30	
5:00		5:00		5:00		5:00	
5:30		5:30		5:30		5:30	
6:00		6:00		6:00		6:00	
6:30		6:30		6:30		6:30	
7:00		7:00		7:00		7:00	
7:30		7:30		7:30		7:30	
8:00		8:00		8:00		8:00	
8:30		8:30		8:30		8:30	
9:00		9:00		9:00		9:00	
9:30		9:30		9:30		9:30	
10:00		10:00		10:00		10:00	
10:30		10:30		10:30		10:30	

1	2	3	4	5	1	2	3	4	5	1	2	3	4	5	1	2	3	4	5
TASKS					**TASKS**					**TASKS**					**TASKS**				

17

Plan Your Work
Then Work Your Plan

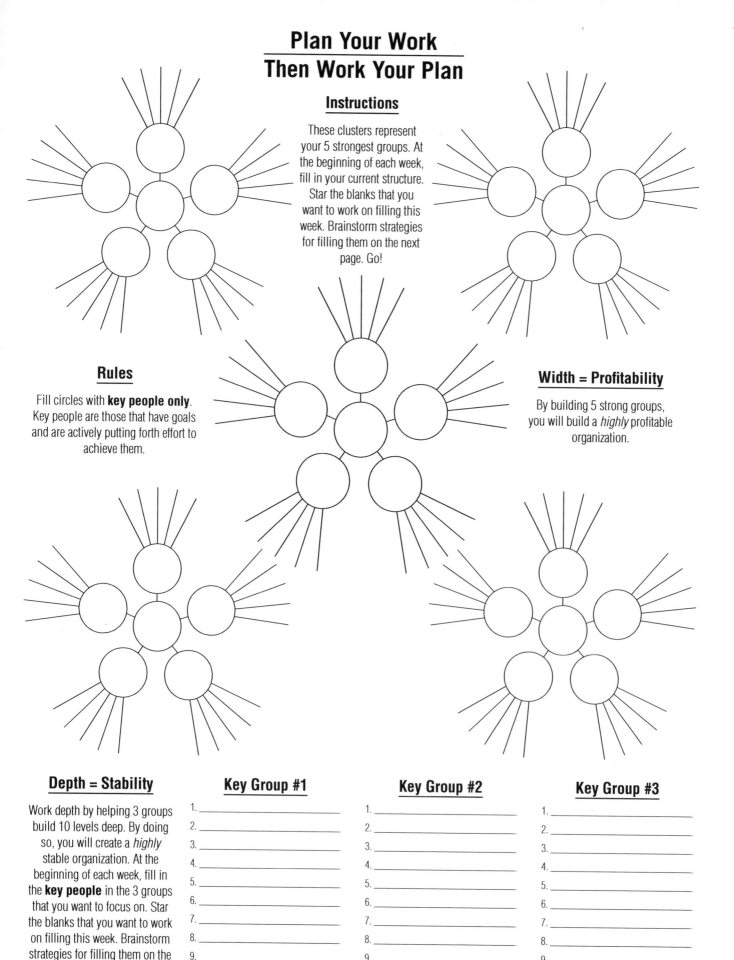

Instructions

These clusters represent your 5 strongest groups. At the beginning of each week, fill in your current structure. Star the blanks that you want to work on filling this week. Brainstorm strategies for filling them on the next page. Go!

Rules

Fill circles with **key people only**. Key people are those that have goals and are actively putting forth effort to achieve them.

Width = Profitability

By building 5 strong groups, you will build a *highly* profitable organization.

Depth = Stability

Work depth by helping 3 groups build 10 levels deep. By doing so, you will create a *highly* stable organization. At the beginning of each week, fill in the **key people** in the 3 groups that you want to focus on. Star the blanks that you want to work on filling this week. Brainstorm strategies for filling them on the next page. Go!

Key Group #1

1. _____
2. _____
3. _____
4. _____
5. _____
6. _____
7. _____
8. _____
9. _____
10. _____

Key Group #2

1. _____
2. _____
3. _____
4. _____
5. _____
6. _____
7. _____
8. _____
9. _____
10. _____

Key Group #3

1. _____
2. _____
3. _____
4. _____
5. _____
6. _____
7. _____
8. _____
9. _____
10. _____

Where to Focus My Efforts

Date _____   Current Rank _____   Current Volume $_____

Tasks

WEEK FROM / TO /	MONDAY TASKS	TUESDAY TASKS	WEDNESDAY TASKS
THIS WEEK'S PRIORITIES			
1	1	1	1
2	2	2	2
3	3	3	3
4	4	4	4
5	5	5	5
6	6	6	6
7	7	7	7
8	8	8	8
	5:00	5:00	5:00
	5:30	5:30	5:30
	6:00	6:00	6:00
	6:30	6:30	6:30
	7:00	7:00	7:00
	7:30	7:30	7:30
	8:00	8:00	8:00
	8:30	8:30	8:30
	9:00	9:00	9:00
	9:30	9:30	9:30
	10:00	10:00	10:00
	10:30	10:30	10:30
	11:00	11:00	11:00
	11:30	11:30	11:30
	12:00p	12:00p	12:00p
	12:30	12:30	12:30
	1:00	1:00	1:00
	1:30	1:30	1:30
	2:00	2:00	2:00
	2:30	2:30	2:30
	3:00	3:00	3:00
	3:30	3:30	3:30
	4:00	4:00	4:00
	4:30	4:30	4:30
	5:00	5:00	5:00
	5:30	5:30	5:30
	6:00	6:00	6:00
	6:30	6:30	6:30
	7:00	7:00	7:00
	7:30	7:30	7:30
	8:00	8:00	8:00
	8:30	8:30	8:30
	9:00	9:00	9:00
	9:30	9:30	9:30
	10:00	10:00	10:00
	10:30	10:30	10:30

That's why when people say, 'Zig, motivation doesn't last.' I say... Bathing doesn't either, that's why I recommend it daily!
— Zig Ziglar

TIME FOCUS KEY
1 = Your Miracle Morning
2 = Prospecting
3 = Presenting
4 = Following up
5 = Getting people started

TIME FOCUS:	1	2	3	4	5	1	2	3	4	5	1	2	3	4	5
✔ when completed:															

20

THURSDAY TASKS	FRIDAY TASKS	SATURDAY TASKS	SUNDAY TASKS
1	1	1	1
2	2	2	2
3	3	3	3
4	4	4	4
5	5	5	5
6	6	6	6
7	7	7	7
8	8	8	8
5:00	5:00	5:00	5:00
5:30	5:30	5:30	5:30
6:00	6:00	6:00	6:00
6:30	6:30	6:30	6:30
7:00	7:00	7:00	7:00
7:30	7:30	7:30	7:30
8:00	8:00	8:00	8:00
8:30	8:30	8:30	8:30
9:00	9:00	9:00	9:00
9:30	9:30	9:30	9:30
10:00	10:00	10:00	10:00
10:30	10:30	10:30	10:30
11:00	11:00	11:00	11:00
11:30	11:30	11:30	11:30
12:00p	12:00p	12:00p	12:00p
12:30	12:30	12:30	12:30
1:00	1:00	1:00	1:00
1:30	1:30	1:30	1:30
2:00	2:00	2:00	2:00
2:30	2:30	2:30	2:30
3:00	3:00	3:00	3:00
3:30	3:30	3:30	3:30
4:00	4:00	4:00	4:00
4:30	4:30	4:30	4:30
5:00	5:00	5:00	5:00
5:30	5:30	5:30	5:30
6:00	6:00	6:00	6:00
6:30	6:30	6:30	6:30
7:00	7:00	7:00	7:00
7:30	7:30	7:30	7:30
8:00	8:00	8:00	8:00
8:30	8:30	8:30	8:30
9:00	9:00	9:00	9:00
9:30	9:30	9:30	9:30
10:00	10:00	10:00	10:00
10:30	10:30	10:30	10:30

1	2	3	4	5	1	2	3	4	5	1	2	3	4	5	1	2	3	4	5
TASKS					TASKS					TASKS					TASKS				

Plan Your Work
Then Work Your Plan

Instructions

These clusters represent your 5 strongest groups. At the beginning of each week, fill in your current structure. Star the blanks that you want to work on filling this week. Brainstorm strategies for filling them on the next page. Go!

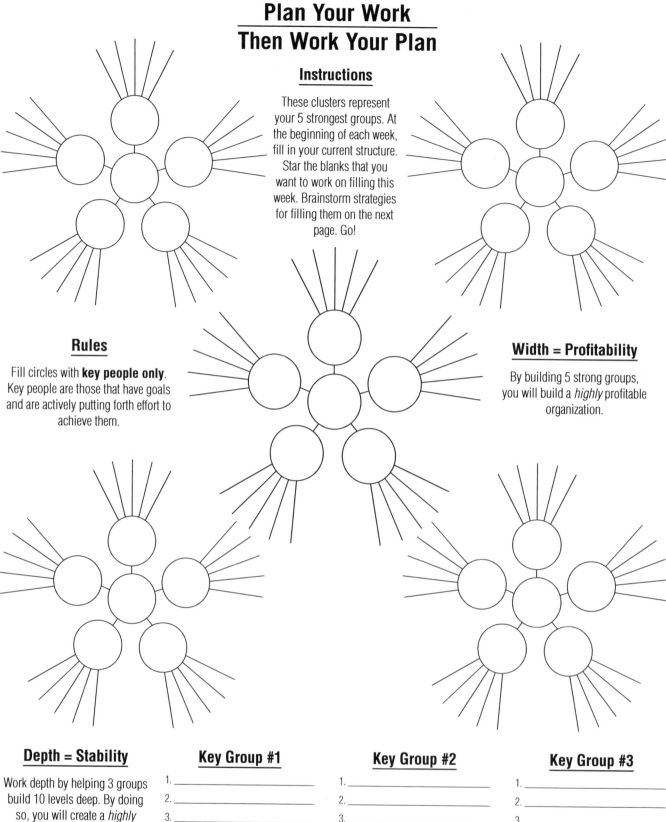

Rules

Fill circles with **key people only**. Key people are those that have goals and are actively putting forth effort to achieve them.

Width = Profitability

By building 5 strong groups, you will build a *highly* profitable organization.

Depth = Stability

Work depth by helping 3 groups build 10 levels deep. By doing so, you will create a *highly* stable organization. At the beginning of each week, fill in the **key people** in the 3 groups that you want to focus on. Star the blanks that you want to work on filling this week. Brainstorm strategies for filling them on the next page. Go!

Key Group #1
1. _____
2. _____
3. _____
4. _____
5. _____
6. _____
7. _____
8. _____
9. _____
10. _____

Key Group #2
1. _____
2. _____
3. _____
4. _____
5. _____
6. _____
7. _____
8. _____
9. _____
10. _____

Key Group #3
1. _____
2. _____
3. _____
4. _____
5. _____
6. _____
7. _____
8. _____
9. _____
10. _____

Where to Focus My Efforts

Date _____   Current Rank _____   Current Volume $ _____

Tasks

_____

_____

_____

_____

_____

_____

_____

_____

_____

_____

_____

_____

_____

_____

_____

_____

_____

_____

_____

_____

_____

_____

_____

_____

_____

WEEK FROM / TO /	MONDAY TASKS	TUESDAY TASKS	WEDNESDAY TASKS
THIS WEEK'S PRIORITIES			
1	1	1	1
2	2	2	2
3	3	3	3
4	4	4	4
5	5	5	5
6	6	6	6
7	7	7	7
8	8	8	8
	5:00	5:00	5:00
	5:30	5:30	5:30
	6:00	6:00	6:00
	6:30	6:30	6:30
	7:00	7:00	7:00
	7:30	7:30	7:30
	8:00	8:00	8:00
	8:30	8:30	8:30
	9:00	9:00	9:00
	9:30	9:30	9:30
	10:00	10:00	10:00
	10:30	10:30	10:30
	11:00	11:00	11:00
	11:30	11:30	11:30
	12:00p	12:00p	12:00p
	12:30	12:30	12:30
	1:00	1:00	1:00
	1:30	1:30	1:30
	2:00	2:00	2:00
	2:30	2:30	2:30
	3:00	3:00	3:00
	3:30	3:30	3:30
	4:00	4:00	4:00
	4:30	4:30	4:30
	5:00	5:00	5:00
	5:30	5:30	5:30
	6:00	6:00	6:00
	6:30	6:30	6:30
	7:00	7:00	7:00
	7:30	7:30	7:30
	8:00	8:00	8:00
	8:30	8:30	8:30
	9:00	9:00	9:00
	9:30	9:30	9:30
	10:00	10:00	10:00
	10:30	10:30	10:30

> *The pessimist sees difficulty in every opportunity. The optimist sees opportunity in every difficulty.*
> —Winston Churchill

TIME FOCUS KEY
1 = Your Miracle Morning
2 = Prospecting
3 = Presenting
4 = Following up
5 = Getting people started

TIME FOCUS:	1	2	3	4	5	1	2	3	4	5	1	2	3	4	5
✔ when completed:															

THURSDAY	FRIDAY	SATURDAY	SUNDAY
TASKS	**TASKS**	**TASKS**	**TASKS**
1	1	1	1
2	2	2	2
3	3	3	3
4	4	4	4
5	5	5	5
6	6	6	6
7	7	7	7
8	8	8	8
5:00	5:00	5:00	5:00
5:30	5:30	5:30	5:30
6:00	6:00	6:00	6:00
6:30	6:30	6:30	6:30
7:00	7:00	7:00	7:00
7:30	7:30	7:30	7:30
8:00	8:00	8:00	8:00
8:30	8:30	8:30	8:30
9:00	9:00	9:00	9:00
9:30	9:30	9:30	9:30
10:00	10:00	10:00	10:00
10:30	10:30	10:30	10:30
11:00	11:00	11:00	11:00
11:30	11:30	11:30	11:30
12:00p	12:00p	12:00p	12:00p
12:30	12:30	12:30	12:30
1:00	1:00	1:00	1:00
1:30	1:30	1:30	1:30
2:00	2:00	2:00	2:00
2:30	2:30	2:30	2:30
3:00	3:00	3:00	3:00
3:30	3:30	3:30	3:30
4:00	4:00	4:00	4:00
4:30	4:30	4:30	4:30
5:00	5:00	5:00	5:00
5:30	5:30	5:30	5:30
6:00	6:00	6:00	6:00
6:30	6:30	6:30	6:30
7:00	7:00	7:00	7:00
7:30	7:30	7:30	7:30
8:00	8:00	8:00	8:00
8:30	8:30	8:30	8:30
9:00	9:00	9:00	9:00
9:30	9:30	9:30	9:30
10:00	10:00	10:00	10:00
10:30	10:30	10:30	10:30

1	2	3	4	5	1	2	3	4	5	1	2	3	4	5	1	2	3	4	5
		TASKS					**TASKS**					**TASKS**					**TASKS**		

Plan Your Work
Then Work Your Plan

Instructions

These clusters represent your 5 strongest groups. At the beginning of each week, fill in your current structure. Star the blanks that you want to work on filling this week. Brainstorm strategies for filling them on the next page. Go!

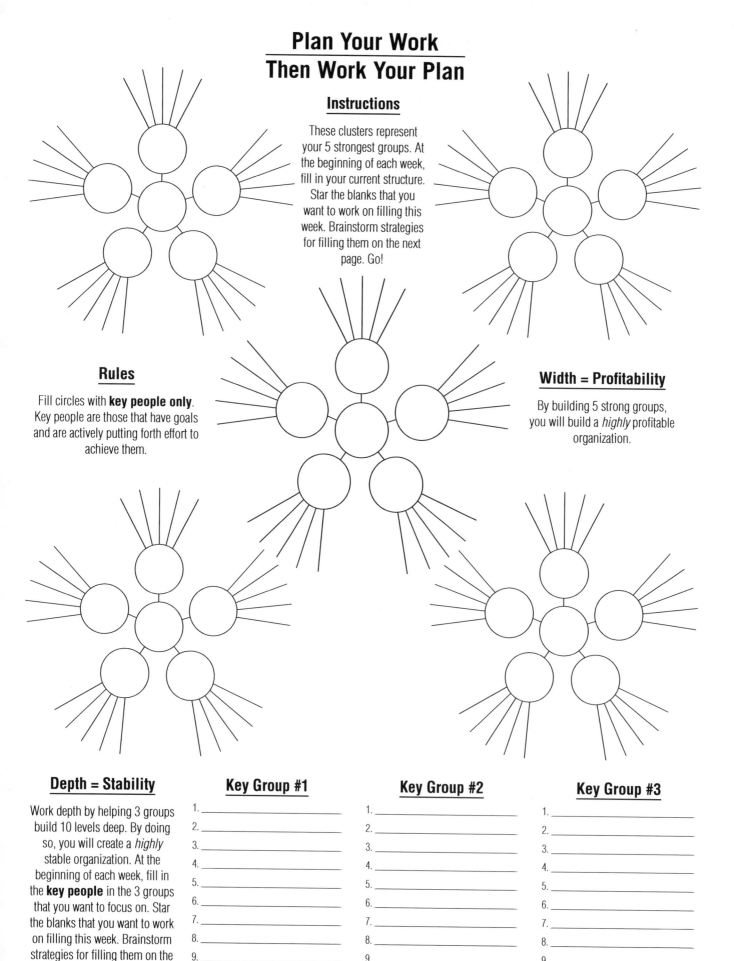

Rules

Fill circles with **key people only**. Key people are those that have goals and are actively putting forth effort to achieve them.

Width = Profitability

By building 5 strong groups, you will build a *highly* profitable organization.

Depth = Stability

Work depth by helping 3 groups build 10 levels deep. By doing so, you will create a *highly* stable organization. At the beginning of each week, fill in the **key people** in the 3 groups that you want to focus on. Star the blanks that you want to work on filling this week. Brainstorm strategies for filling them on the next page. Go!

Key Group #1

1. _____
2. _____
3. _____
4. _____
5. _____
6. _____
7. _____
8. _____
9. _____
10. _____

Key Group #2

1. _____
2. _____
3. _____
4. _____
5. _____
6. _____
7. _____
8. _____
9. _____
10. _____

Key Group #3

1. _____
2. _____
3. _____
4. _____
5. _____
6. _____
7. _____
8. _____
9. _____
10. _____

Where to Focus My Efforts

Date _____ Current Rank _____ Current Volume _$_____

Tasks

_____

_____

_____

_____

_____

_____

_____

_____

_____

_____

_____

_____

_____

_____

_____

_____

_____

_____

_____

_____

_____

_____

_____

_____

_____

_____

Priorities	Monday Tasks	Tuesday Tasks	Wednesday Tasks
1	1	1	1
2	2	2	2
3	3	3	3
4	4	4	4
5	5	5	5
6	6	6	6
7	7	7	7
8	8	8	8

	Monday	Tuesday	Wednesday
	5:00	5:00	5:00
	5:30	5:30	5:30
	6:00	6:00	6:00
	6:30	6:30	6:30
	7:00	7:00	7:00
	7:30	7:30	7:30
	8:00	8:00	8:00
	8:30	8:30	8:30
	9:00	9:00	9:00
	9:30	9:30	9:30
	10:00	10:00	10:00
	10:30	10:30	10:30
	11:00	11:00	11:00
	11:30	11:30	11:30
	12:00p	12:00p	12:00p
	12:30	12:30	12:30
	1:00	1:00	1:00
	1:30	1:30	1:30
	2:00	2:00	2:00
	2:30	2:30	2:30
	3:00	3:00	3:00
	3:30	3:30	3:30
	4:00	4:00	4:00
	4:30	4:30	4:30
	5:00	5:00	5:00
	5:30	5:30	5:30
	6:00	6:00	6:00
	6:30	6:30	6:30
	7:00	7:00	7:00
	7:30	7:30	7:30
	8:00	8:00	8:00
	8:30	8:30	8:30
	9:00	9:00	9:00
	9:30	9:30	9:30
	10:00	10:00	10:00
	10:30	10:30	10:30

If you don't build your dream, someone else will hire you to help them build theirs.
— Dhirubhai Ambani

TIME FOCUS KEY

| 1 = Your Miracle Morning |
| 2 = Prospecting |
| 3 = Presenting |
| 4 = Following up |
| 5 = Getting people started |

TIME FOCUS:	1	2	3	4	5	1	2	3	4	5	1	2	3	4	5
✔ when completed:															

THURSDAY	FRIDAY	SATURDAY	SUNDAY
TASKS	**TASKS**	**TASKS**	**TASKS**
1	1	1	1
2	2	2	2
3	3	3	3
4	4	4	4
5	5	5	5
6	6	6	6
7	7	7	7
8	8	8	8
5:00	5:00	5:00	5:00
5:30	5:30	5:30	5:30
6:00	6:00	6:00	6:00
6:30	6:30	6:30	6:30
7:00	7:00	7:00	7:00
7:30	7:30	7:30	7:30
8:00	8:00	8:00	8:00
8:30	8:30	8:30	8:30
9:00	9:00	9:00	9:00
9:30	9:30	9:30	9:30
10:00	10:00	10:00	10:00
10:30	10:30	10:30	10:30
11:00	11:00	11:00	11:00
11:30	11:30	11:30	11:30
12:00p	12:00p	12:00p	12:00p
12:30	12:30	12:30	12:30
1:00	1:00	1:00	1:00
1:30	1:30	1:30	1:30
2:00	2:00	2:00	2:00
2:30	2:30	2:30	2:30
3:00	3:00	3:00	3:00
3:30	3:30	3:30	3:30
4:00	4:00	4:00	4:00
4:30	4:30	4:30	4:30
5:00	5:00	5:00	5:00
5:30	5:30	5:30	5:30
6:00	6:00	6:00	6:00
6:30	6:30	6:30	6:30
7:00	7:00	7:00	7:00
7:30	7:30	7:30	7:30
8:00	8:00	8:00	8:00
8:30	8:30	8:30	8:30
9:00	9:00	9:00	9:00
9:30	9:30	9:30	9:30
10:00	10:00	10:00	10:00
10:30	10:30	10:30	10:30

1	2	3	4	5	1	2	3	4	5	1	2	3	4	5	1	2	3	4	5
TASKS					**TASKS**					**TASKS**					**TASKS**				

Plan Your Work
Then Work Your Plan

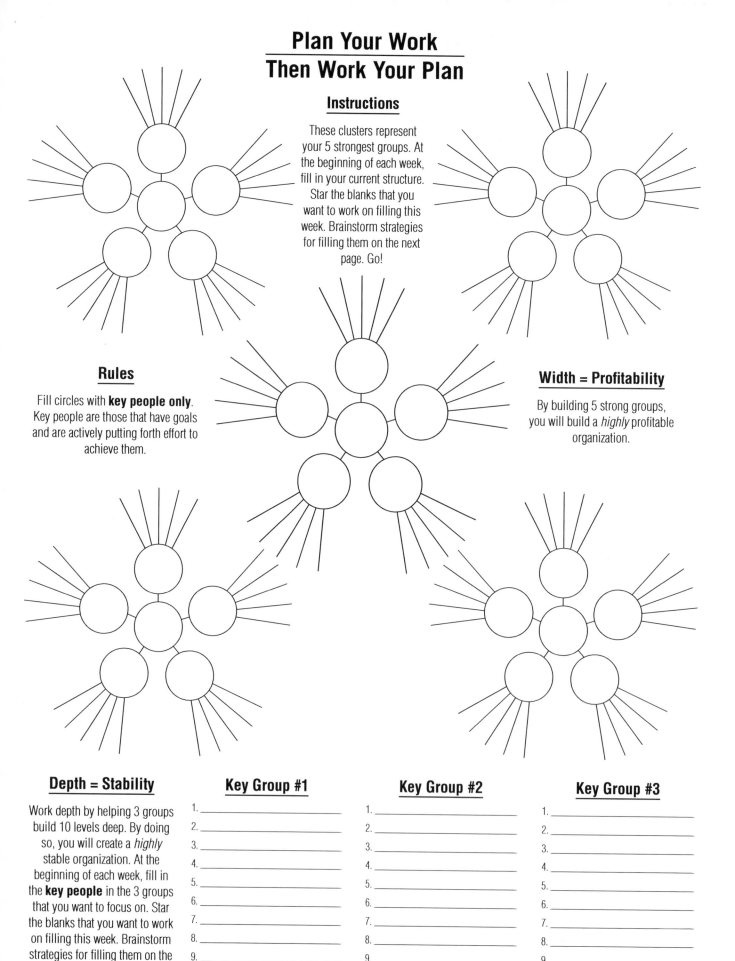

Instructions

These clusters represent your 5 strongest groups. At the beginning of each week, fill in your current structure. Star the blanks that you want to work on filling this week. Brainstorm strategies for filling them on the next page. Go!

Rules

Fill circles with **key people only**. Key people are those that have goals and are actively putting forth effort to achieve them.

Width = Profitability

By building 5 strong groups, you will build a *highly* profitable organization.

Depth = Stability

Work depth by helping 3 groups build 10 levels deep. By doing so, you will create a *highly* stable organization. At the beginning of each week, fill in the **key people** in the 3 groups that you want to focus on. Star the blanks that you want to work on filling this week. Brainstorm strategies for filling them on the next page. Go!

Key Group #1

1. _____
2. _____
3. _____
4. _____
5. _____
6. _____
7. _____
8. _____
9. _____
10. _____

Key Group #2

1. _____
2. _____
3. _____
4. _____
5. _____
6. _____
7. _____
8. _____
9. _____
10. _____

Key Group #3

1. _____
2. _____
3. _____
4. _____
5. _____
6. _____
7. _____
8. _____
9. _____
10. _____

Where to Focus My Efforts

Date _____   Current Rank _____   Current Volume $_____

Tasks

WEEK FROM __/__ TO __/__	MONDAY TASKS	TUESDAY TASKS	WEDNESDAY TASKS
THIS WEEK'S PRIORITIES			
1	1	1	1
2	2	2	2
3	3	3	3
4	4	4	4
5	5	5	5
6	6	6	6
7	7	7	7
8	8	8	8
	5:00	5:00	5:00
	5:30	5:30	5:30
	6:00	6:00	6:00
	6:30	6:30	6:30
	7:00	7:00	7:00
	7:30	7:30	7:30
	8:00	8:00	8:00
	8:30	8:30	8:30
	9:00	9:00	9:00
	9:30	9:30	9:30
	10:00	10:00	10:00
	10:30	10:30	10:30
	11:00	11:00	11:00
	11:30	11:30	11:30
	12:00p	12:00p	12:00p
	12:30	12:30	12:30
	1:00	1:00	1:00
	1:30	1:30	1:30
	2:00	2:00	2:00
	2:30	2:30	2:30
	3:00	3:00	3:00
	3:30	3:30	3:30
	4:00	4:00	4:00
	4:30	4:30	4:30
	5:00	5:00	5:00
	5:30	5:30	5:30
	6:00	6:00	6:00
	6:30	6:30	6:30
	7:00	7:00	7:00
	7:30	7:30	7:30
	8:00	8:00	8:00
	8:30	8:30	8:30
	9:00	9:00	9:00
	9:30	9:30	9:30
	10:00	10:00	10:00
	10:30	10:30	10:30

The best time to get started was yesterday, but the second best time is today!

TIME FOCUS KEY
1 = Your Miracle Morning
2 = Prospecting
3 = Presenting
4 = Following up
5 = Getting people started

TIME FOCUS:	1	2	3	4	5	1	2	3	4	5	1	2	3	4	5
✔ when completed:															

THURSDAY		FRIDAY		SATURDAY		SUNDAY	
TASKS		**TASKS**		**TASKS**		**TASKS**	
1		1		1		1	
2		2		2		2	
3		3		3		3	
4		4		4		4	
5		5		5		5	
6		6		6		6	
7		7		7		7	
8		8		8		8	
5:00		5:00		5:00		5:00	
5:30		5:30		5:30		5:30	
6:00		6:00		6:00		6:00	
6:30		6:30		6:30		6:30	
7:00		7:00		7:00		7:00	
7:30		7:30		7:30		7:30	
8:00		8:00		8:00		8:00	
8:30		8:30		8:30		8:30	
9:00		9:00		9:00		9:00	
9:30		9:30		9:30		9:30	
10:00		10:00		10:00		10:00	
10:30		10:30		10:30		10:30	
11:00		11:00		11:00		11:00	
11:30		11:30		11:30		11:30	
12:00p		12:00p		12:00p		12:00p	
12:30		12:30		12:30		12:30	
1:00		1:00		1:00		1:00	
1:30		1:30		1:30		1:30	
2:00		2:00		2:00		2:00	
2:30		2:30		2:30		2:30	
3:00		3:00		3:00		3:00	
3:30		3:30		3:30		3:30	
4:00		4:00		4:00		4:00	
4:30		4:30		4:30		4:30	
5:00		5:00		5:00		5:00	
5:30		5:30		5:30		5:30	
6:00		6:00		6:00		6:00	
6:30		6:30		6:30		6:30	
7:00		7:00		7:00		7:00	
7:30		7:30		7:30		7:30	
8:00		8:00		8:00		8:00	
8:30		8:30		8:30		8:30	
9:00		9:00		9:00		9:00	
9:30		9:30		9:30		9:30	
10:00		10:00		10:00		10:00	
10:30		10:30		10:30		10:30	

1	2	3	4	5	1	2	3	4	5	1	2	3	4	5	1	2	3	4	5
TASKS					**TASKS**					**TASKS**					**TASKS**				

Plan Your Work
Then Work Your Plan

Instructions

These clusters represent your 5 strongest groups. At the beginning of each week, fill in your current structure. Star the blanks that you want to work on filling this week. Brainstorm strategies for filling them on the next page. Go!

Rules

Fill circles with **key people only**. Key people are those that have goals and are actively putting forth effort to achieve them.

Width = Profitability

By building 5 strong groups, you will build a *highly* profitable organization.

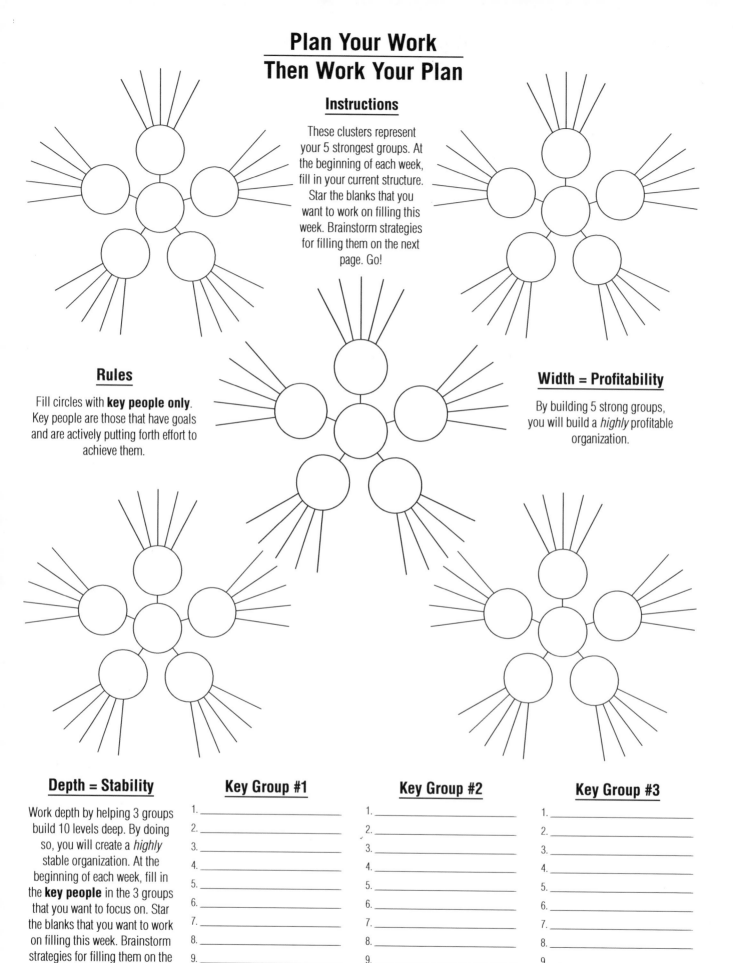

Depth = Stability

Work depth by helping 3 groups build 10 levels deep. By doing so, you will create a *highly* stable organization. At the beginning of each week, fill in the **key people** in the 3 groups that you want to focus on. Star the blanks that you want to work on filling this week. Brainstorm strategies for filling them on the next page. Go!

Key Group #1

1. _____
2. _____
3. _____
4. _____
5. _____
6. _____
7. _____
8. _____
9. _____
10. _____

Key Group #2

1. _____
2. _____
3. _____
4. _____
5. _____
6. _____
7. _____
8. _____
9. _____
10. _____

Key Group #3

1. _____
2. _____
3. _____
4. _____
5. _____
6. _____
7. _____
8. _____
9. _____
10. _____

34

Where to Focus My Efforts

Date _____   Current Rank _____   Current Volume $ _____

Tasks

_____

_____

_____

_____

_____

_____

_____

_____

_____

_____

_____

_____

_____

_____

_____

_____

_____

_____

_____

_____

_____

_____

_____

_____

_____

_____

_____

_____

_____

WEEK FROM / TO /	MONDAY	TUESDAY	WEDNESDAY
THIS WEEK'S PRIORITIES	TASKS	TASKS	TASKS
1	1	1	1
2	2	2	2
3	3	3	3
4	4	4	4
5	5	5	5
6	6	6	6
7	7	7	7
8	8	8	8
	5:00	5:00	5:00
	5:30	5:30	5:30
	6:00	6:00	6:00
	6:30	6:30	6:30
	7:00	7:00	7:00
	7:30	7:30	7:30
	8:00	8:00	8:00
	8:30	8:30	8:30
	9:00	9:00	9:00
	9:30	9:30	9:30
	10:00	10:00	10:00
	10:30	10:30	10:30
	11:00	11:00	11:00
	11:30	11:30	11:30
	12:00p	12:00p	12:00p
	12:30	12:30	12:30
	1:00	1:00	1:00
	1:30	1:30	1:30
	2:00	2:00	2:00
	2:30	2:30	2:30
	3:00	3:00	3:00
	3:30	3:30	3:30
	4:00	4:00	4:00
	4:30	4:30	4:30
	5:00	5:00	5:00
	5:30	5:30	5:30
	6:00	6:00	6:00
	6:30	6:30	6:30
	7:00	7:00	7:00
	7:30	7:30	7:30
	8:00	8:00	8:00
	8:30	8:30	8:30
	9:00	9:00	9:00
	9:30	9:30	9:30
	10:00	10:00	10:00
	10:30	10:30	10:30

You will never change your life until you change something you do daily. The secret of your success is found in your daily routine.
—John Maxwell

TIME FOCUS KEY
1 = Your Miracle Morning
2 = Prospecting
3 = Presenting
4 = Following up
5 = Getting people started

TIME FOCUS:	1	2	3	4	5	1	2	3	4	5	1	2	3	4	5
✔ when completed:															

THURSDAY	FRIDAY	SATURDAY	SUNDAY
1	1	1	1
2	2	2	2
3	3	3	3
4	4	4	4
5	5	5	5
6	6	6	6
7	7	7	7
8	8	8	8
5:00	5:00	5:00	5:00
5:30	5:30	5:30	5:30
6:00	6:00	6:00	6:00
6:30	6:30	6:30	6:30
7:00	7:00	7:00	7:00
7:30	7:30	7:30	7:30
8:00	8:00	8:00	8:00
8:30	8:30	8:30	8:30
9:00	9:00	9:00	9:00
9:30	9:30	9:30	9:30
10:00	10:00	10:00	10:00
10:30	10:30	10:30	10:30
11:00	11:00	11:00	11:00
11:30	11:30	11:30	11:30
12:00p	12:00p	12:00p	12:00p
12:30	12:30	12:30	12:30
1:00	1:00	1:00	1:00
1:30	1:30	1:30	1:30
2:00	2:00	2:00	2:00
2:30	2:30	2:30	2:30
3:00	3:00	3:00	3:00
3:30	3:30	3:30	3:30
4:00	4:00	4:00	4:00
4:30	4:30	4:30	4:30
5:00	5:00	5:00	5:00
5:30	5:30	5:30	5:30
6:00	6:00	6:00	6:00
6:30	6:30	6:30	6:30
7:00	7:00	7:00	7:00
7:30	7:30	7:30	7:30
8:00	8:00	8:00	8:00
8:30	8:30	8:30	8:30
9:00	9:00	9:00	9:00
9:30	9:30	9:30	9:30
10:00	10:00	10:00	10:00
10:30	10:30	10:30	10:30

1	2	3	4	5	1	2	3	4	5	1	2	3	4	5	1	2	3	4	5

Plan Your Work
Then Work Your Plan

Instructions

These clusters represent your 5 strongest groups. At the beginning of each week, fill in your current structure. Star the blanks that you want to work on filling this week. Brainstorm strategies for filling them on the next page. Go!

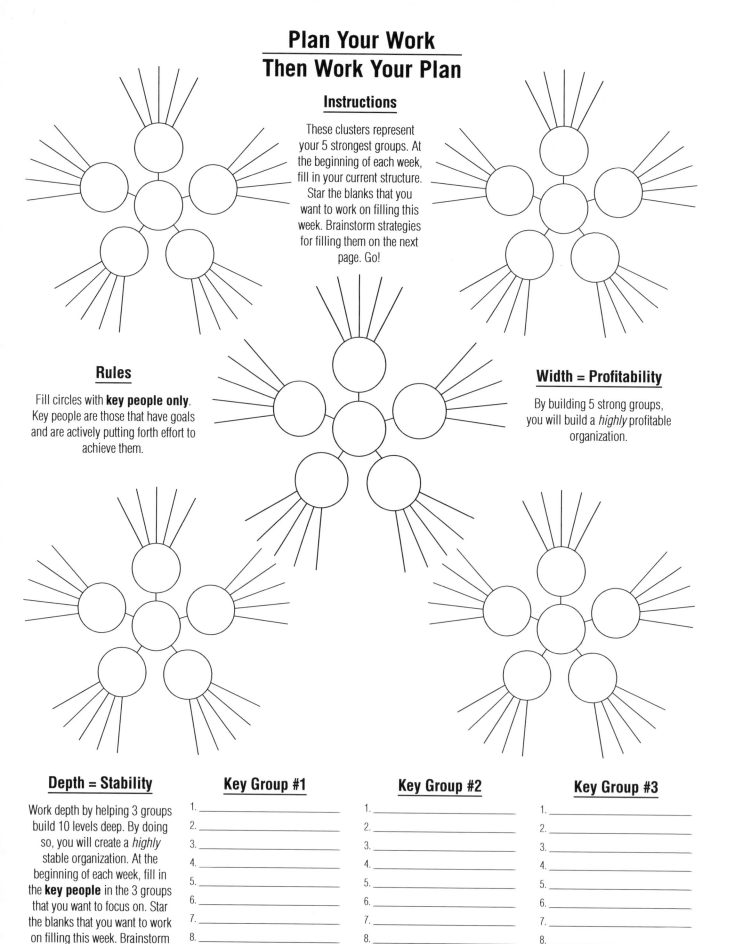

Rules

Fill circles with **key people only**. Key people are those that have goals and are actively putting forth effort to achieve them.

Width = Profitability

By building 5 strong groups, you will build a *highly* profitable organization.

Depth = Stability

Work depth by helping 3 groups build 10 levels deep. By doing so, you will create a *highly* stable organization. At the beginning of each week, fill in the **key people** in the 3 groups that you want to focus on. Star the blanks that you want to work on filling this week. Brainstorm strategies for filling them on the next page. Go!

Key Group #1

1. _____
2. _____
3. _____
4. _____
5. _____
6. _____
7. _____
8. _____
9. _____
10. _____

Key Group #2

1. _____
2. _____
3. _____
4. _____
5. _____
6. _____
7. _____
8. _____
9. _____
10. _____

Key Group #3

1. _____
2. _____
3. _____
4. _____
5. _____
6. _____
7. _____
8. _____
9. _____
10. _____

Where to Focus My Efforts

Date _____ Current Rank _____ Current Volume $_____

Tasks

_____
_____
_____
_____
_____
_____
_____
_____
_____
_____
_____
_____
_____
_____
_____
_____
_____
_____
_____
_____
_____
_____
_____
_____
_____
_____
_____
_____
_____
_____

WEEK FROM	/ TO /	MONDAY		TUESDAY		WEDNESDAY	
THIS WEEK'S PRIORITIES		**TASKS**		**TASKS**		**TASKS**	
1		1		1		1	
2		2		2		2	
3		3		3		3	
4		4		4		4	
5		5		5		5	
6		6		6		6	
7		7		7		7	
8		8		8		8	
		5:00		5:00		5:00	
		5:30		5:30		5:30	
		6:00		6:00		6:00	
		6:30		6:30		6:30	
		7:00		7:00		7:00	
		7:30		7:30		7:30	
		8:00		8:00		8:00	
		8:30		8:30		8:30	
		9:00		9:00		9:00	
		9:30		9:30		9:30	
		10:00		10:00		10:00	
		10:30		10:30		10:30	
		11:00		11:00		11:00	
		11:30		11:30		11:30	
		12:00p		12:00p		12:00p	
		12:30		12:30		12:30	
		1:00		1:00		1:00	
		1:30		1:30		1:30	
		2:00		2:00		2:00	
		2:30		2:30		2:30	
		3:00		3:00		3:00	
		3:30		3:30		3:30	
		4:00		4:00		4:00	
		4:30		4:30		4:30	
		5:00		5:00		5:00	
		5:30		5:30		5:30	
		6:00		6:00		6:00	
		6:30		6:30		6:30	
		7:00		7:00		7:00	
		7:30		7:30		7:30	
		8:00		8:00		8:00	
		8:30		8:30		8:30	
		9:00		9:00		9:00	
		9:30		9:30		9:30	
		10:00		10:00		10:00	
		10:30		10:30		10:30	

When you feel like quitting, think about why you started.

TIME FOCUS KEY

| 1 = Your Miracle Morning |
| 2 = Prospecting |
| 3 = Presenting |
| 4 = Following up |
| 5 = Getting people started |

TIME FOCUS:	1	2	3	4	5	1	2	3	4	5	1	2	3	4	5
✔ when completed:															

THURSDAY TASKS	FRIDAY TASKS	SATURDAY TASKS	SUNDAY TASKS
1	1	1	1
2	2	2	2
3	3	3	3
4	4	4	4
5	5	5	5
6	6	6	6
7	7	7	7
8	8	8	8
5:00	5:00	5:00	5:00
5:30	5:30	5:30	5:30
6:00	6:00	6:00	6:00
6:30	6:30	6:30	6:30
7:00	7:00	7:00	7:00
7:30	7:30	7:30	7:30
8:00	8:00	8:00	8:00
8:30	8:30	8:30	8:30
9:00	9:00	9:00	9:00
9:30	9:30	9:30	9:30
10:00	10:00	10:00	10:00
10:30	10:30	10:30	10:30
11:00	11:00	11:00	11:00
11:30	11:30	11:30	11:30
12:00p	12:00p	12:00p	12:00p
12:30	12:30	12:30	12:30
1:00	1:00	1:00	1:00
1:30	1:30	1:30	1:30
2:00	2:00	2:00	2:00
2:30	2:30	2:30	2:30
3:00	3:00	3:00	3:00
3:30	3:30	3:30	3:30
4:00	4:00	4:00	4:00
4:30	4:30	4:30	4:30
5:00	5:00	5:00	5:00
5:30	5:30	5:30	5:30
6:00	6:00	6:00	6:00
6:30	6:30	6:30	6:30
7:00	7:00	7:00	7:00
7:30	7:30	7:30	7:30
8:00	8:00	8:00	8:00
8:30	8:30	8:30	8:30
9:00	9:00	9:00	9:00
9:30	9:30	9:30	9:30
10:00	10:00	10:00	10:00
10:30	10:30	10:30	10:30

1	2	3	4	5	1	2	3	4	5	1	2	3	4	5	1	2	3	4	5
TASKS					TASKS					TASKS					TASKS				

Plan Your Work
Then Work Your Plan

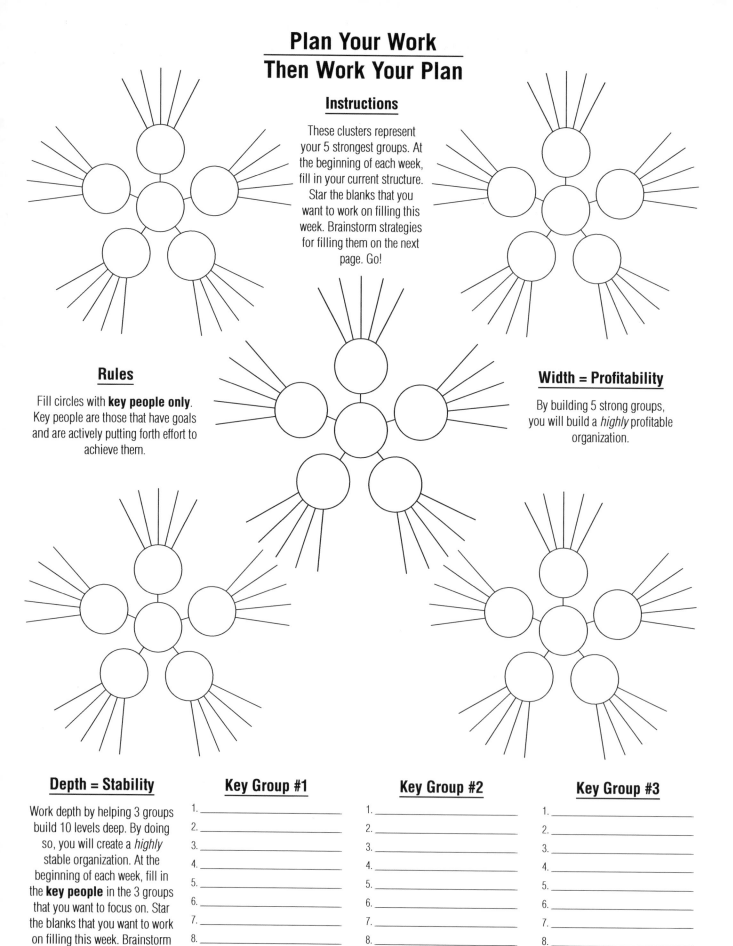

Instructions

These clusters represent your 5 strongest groups. At the beginning of each week, fill in your current structure. Star the blanks that you want to work on filling this week. Brainstorm strategies for filling them on the next page. Go!

Rules

Fill circles with **key people only**. Key people are those that have goals and are actively putting forth effort to achieve them.

Width = Profitability

By building 5 strong groups, you will build a *highly* profitable organization.

Depth = Stability

Work depth by helping 3 groups build 10 levels deep. By doing so, you will create a *highly* stable organization. At the beginning of each week, fill in the **key people** in the 3 groups that you want to focus on. Star the blanks that you want to work on filling this week. Brainstorm strategies for filling them on the next page. Go!

Key Group #1

1. _____
2. _____
3. _____
4. _____
5. _____
6. _____
7. _____
8. _____
9. _____
10. _____

Key Group #2

1. _____
2. _____
3. _____
4. _____
5. _____
6. _____
7. _____
8. _____
9. _____
10. _____

Key Group #3

1. _____
2. _____
3. _____
4. _____
5. _____
6. _____
7. _____
8. _____
9. _____
10. _____

Where to Focus My Efforts

Date _____ Current Rank _____ Current Volume $_____

Tasks

_____

_____

_____

_____

_____

_____

_____

_____

_____

_____

_____

_____

_____

_____

_____

_____

_____

_____

_____

_____

_____

_____

_____

_____

_____

_____

_____

_____

THIS WEEK'S PRIORITIES	MONDAY TASKS	TUESDAY TASKS	WEDNESDAY TASKS
1	1	1	1
2	2	2	2
3	3	3	3
4	4	4	4
5	5	5	5
6	6	6	6
7	7	7	7
8	8	8	8
	5:00	5:00	5:00
	5:30	5:30	5:30
	6:00	6:00	6:00
	6:30	6:30	6:30
	7:00	7:00	7:00
	7:30	7:30	7:30
	8:00	8:00	8:00
	8:30	8:30	8:30
	9:00	9:00	9:00
	9:30	9:30	9:30
	10:00	10:00	10:00
	10:30	10:30	10:30
	11:00	11:00	11:00
	11:30	11:30	11:30
	12:00p	12:00p	12:00p
	12:30	12:30	12:30
	1:00	1:00	1:00
	1:30	1:30	1:30
	2:00	2:00	2:00
	2:30	2:30	2:30
	3:00	3:00	3:00
	3:30	3:30	3:30
	4:00	4:00	4:00
	4:30	4:30	4:30
	5:00	5:00	5:00
	5:30	5:30	5:30
	6:00	6:00	6:00
	6:30	6:30	6:30
	7:00	7:00	7:00
	7:30	7:30	7:30
	8:00	8:00	8:00
	8:30	8:30	8:30
	9:00	9:00	9:00
	9:30	9:30	9:30
	10:00	10:00	10:00
	10:30	10:30	10:30

Work on yourself more than you do on your job.
—Jim Rohn

TIME FOCUS KEY

| 1 = Your Miracle Morning |
| 2 = Prospecting |
| 3 = Presenting |
| 4 = Following up |
| 5 = Getting people started |

TIME FOCUS:	1	2	3	4	5	1	2	3	4	5	1	2	3	4	5
✔ when completed:															

THURSDAY	FRIDAY	SATURDAY	SUNDAY
TASKS	**TASKS**	**TASKS**	**TASKS**
1	1	1	1
2	2	2	2
3	3	3	3
4	4	4	4
5	5	5	5
6	6	6	6
7	7	7	7
8	8	8	8
5:00	5:00	5:00	5:00
5:30	5:30	5:30	5:30
6:00	6:00	6:00	6:00
6:30	6:30	6:30	6:30
7:00	7:00	7:00	7:00
7:30	7:30	7:30	7:30
8:00	8:00	8:00	8:00
8:30	8:30	8:30	8:30
9:00	9:00	9:00	9:00
9:30	9:30	9:30	9:30
10:00	10:00	10:00	10:00
10:30	10:30	10:30	10:30
11:00	11:00	11:00	11:00
11:30	11:30	11:30	11:30
12:00p	12:00p	12:00p	12:00p
12:30	12:30	12:30	12:30
1:00	1:00	1:00	1:00
1:30	1:30	1:30	1:30
2:00	2:00	2:00	2:00
2:30	2:30	2:30	2:30
3:00	3:00	3:00	3:00
3:30	3:30	3:30	3:30
4:00	4:00	4:00	4:00
4:30	4:30	4:30	4:30
5:00	5:00	5:00	5:00
5:30	5:30	5:30	5:30
6:00	6:00	6:00	6:00
6:30	6:30	6:30	6:30
7:00	7:00	7:00	7:00
7:30	7:30	7:30	7:30
8:00	8:00	8:00	8:00
8:30	8:30	8:30	8:30
9:00	9:00	9:00	9:00
9:30	9:30	9:30	9:30
10:00	10:00	10:00	10:00
10:30	10:30	10:30	10:30

1	2	3	4	5	1	2	3	4	5	1	2	3	4	5	1	2	3	4	5
TASKS					**TASKS**					**TASKS**					**TASKS**				

Plan Your Work
Then Work Your Plan

Instructions

These clusters represent your 5 strongest groups. At the beginning of each week, fill in your current structure. Star the blanks that you want to work on filling this week. Brainstorm strategies for filling them on the next page. Go!

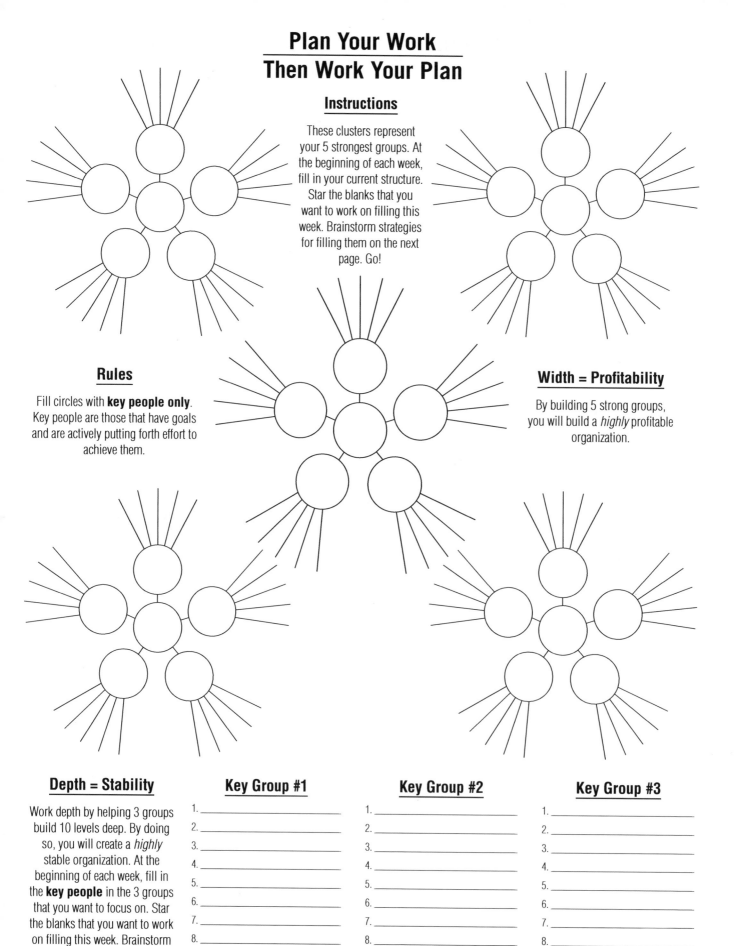

Rules

Fill circles with **key people only**. Key people are those that have goals and are actively putting forth effort to achieve them.

Width = Profitability

By building 5 strong groups, you will build a *highly* profitable organization.

Depth = Stability

Work depth by helping 3 groups build 10 levels deep. By doing so, you will create a *highly* stable organization. At the beginning of each week, fill in the **key people** in the 3 groups that you want to focus on. Star the blanks that you want to work on filling this week. Brainstorm strategies for filling them on the next page. Go!

Key Group #1
1. _____
2. _____
3. _____
4. _____
5. _____
6. _____
7. _____
8. _____
9. _____
10. _____

Key Group #2
1. _____
2. _____
3. _____
4. _____
5. _____
6. _____
7. _____
8. _____
9. _____
10. _____

Key Group #3
1. _____
2. _____
3. _____
4. _____
5. _____
6. _____
7. _____
8. _____
9. _____
10. _____

Where to Focus My Efforts

Date _____   Current Rank _____   Current Volume __$_____

Tasks

WEEK FROM	/ TO /	MONDAY		TUESDAY		WEDNESDAY	
THIS WEEK'S PRIORITIES		**TASKS**		**TASKS**		**TASKS**	
1		1		1		1	
2		2		2		2	
3		3		3		3	
4		4		4		4	
5		5		5		5	
6		6		6		6	
7		7		7		7	
8		8		8		8	

	MONDAY	TUESDAY	WEDNESDAY
	5:00	5:00	5:00
	5:30	5:30	5:30
	6:00	6:00	6:00
	6:30	6:30	6:30
	7:00	7:00	7:00
	7:30	7:30	7:30
	8:00	8:00	8:00
	8:30	8:30	8:30
	9:00	9:00	9:00
	9:30	9:30	9:30
	10:00	10:00	10:00
	10:30	10:30	10:30
	11:00	11:00	11:00
	11:30	11:30	11:30
	12:00p	12:00p	12:00p
	12:30	12:30	12:30
	1:00	1:00	1:00
	1:30	1:30	1:30
	2:00	2:00	2:00
	2:30	2:30	2:30
	3:00	3:00	3:00
	3:30	3:30	3:30
	4:00	4:00	4:00
	4:30	4:30	4:30
	5:00	5:00	5:00
	5:30	5:30	5:30
	6:00	6:00	6:00
	6:30	6:30	6:30
	7:00	7:00	7:00
	7:30	7:30	7:30
	8:00	8:00	8:00
	8:30	8:30	8:30
	9:00	9:00	9:00
	9:30	9:30	9:30
	10:00	10:00	10:00
	10:30	10:30	10:30

You don't build a business. You build people, and then people build the business.
—Zig Ziglar

TIME FOCUS KEY
1 = Your Miracle Morning
2 = Prospecting
3 = Presenting
4 = Following up
5 = Getting people started

TIME FOCUS:	1	2	3	4	5	1	2	3	4	5	1	2	3	4	5
✓ when completed:															

THURSDAY	FRIDAY	SATURDAY	SUNDAY
TASKS	**TASKS**	**TASKS**	**TASKS**
1	1	1	1
2	2	2	2
3	3	3	3
4	4	4	4
5	5	5	5
6	6	6	6
7	7	7	7
8	8	8	8
5:00	5:00	5:00	5:00
5:30	5:30	5:30	5:30
6:00	6:00	6:00	6:00
6:30	6:30	6:30	6:30
7:00	7:00	7:00	7:00
7:30	7:30	7:30	7:30
8:00	8:00	8:00	8:00
8:30	8:30	8:30	8:30
9:00	9:00	9:00	9:00
9:30	9:30	9:30	9:30
10:00	10:00	10:00	10:00
10:30	10:30	10:30	10:30
11:00	11:00	11:00	11:00
11:30	11:30	11:30	11:30
12:00p	12:00p	12:00p	12:00p
12:30	12:30	12:30	12:30
1:00	1:00	1:00	1:00
1:30	1:30	1:30	1:30
2:00	2:00	2:00	2:00
2:30	2:30	2:30	2:30
3:00	3:00	3:00	3:00
3:30	3:30	3:30	3:30
4:00	4:00	4:00	4:00
4:30	4:30	4:30	4:30
5:00	5:00	5:00	5:00
5:30	5:30	5:30	5:30
6:00	6:00	6:00	6:00
6:30	6:30	6:30	6:30
7:00	7:00	7:00	7:00
7:30	7:30	7:30	7:30
8:00	8:00	8:00	8:00
8:30	8:30	8:30	8:30
9:00	9:00	9:00	9:00
9:30	9:30	9:30	9:30
10:00	10:00	10:00	10:00
10:30	10:30	10:30	10:30

1	2	3	4	5	1	2	3	4	5	1	2	3	4	5	1	2	3	4	5
TASKS					**TASKS**					**TASKS**					**TASKS**				

Plan Your Work
Then Work Your Plan

Instructions

These clusters represent your 5 strongest groups. At the beginning of each week, fill in your current structure. Star the blanks that you want to work on filling this week. Brainstorm strategies for filling them on the next page. Go!

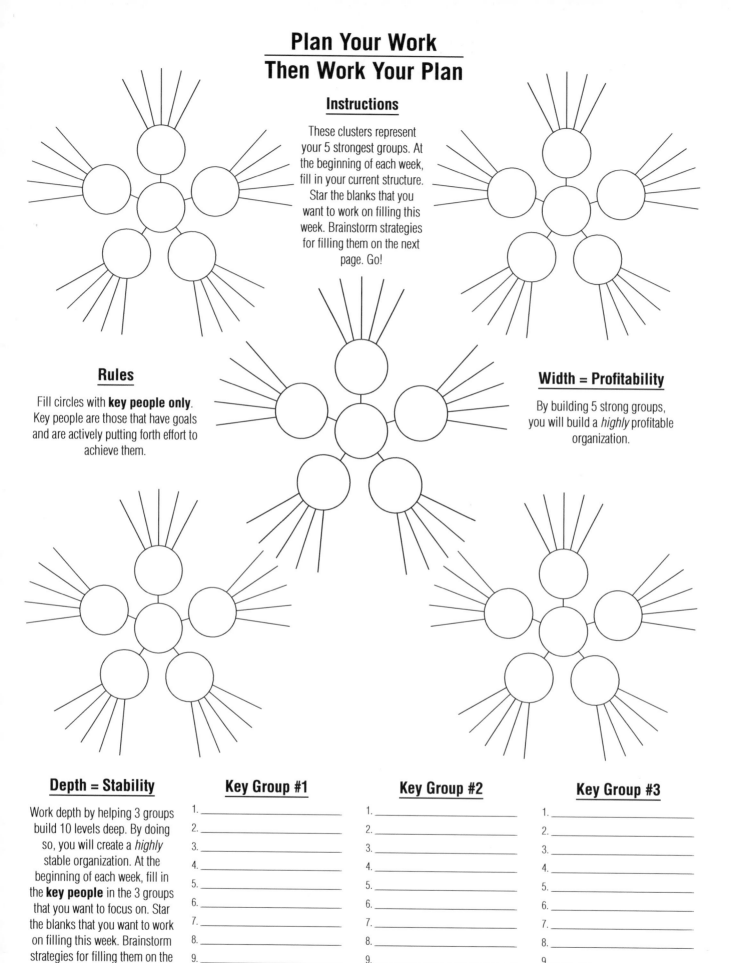

Rules

Fill circles with **key people only**. Key people are those that have goals and are actively putting forth effort to achieve them.

Width = Profitability

By building 5 strong groups, you will build a *highly* profitable organization.

Depth = Stability

Work depth by helping 3 groups build 10 levels deep. By doing so, you will create a *highly* stable organization. At the beginning of each week, fill in the **key people** in the 3 groups that you want to focus on. Star the blanks that you want to work on filling this week. Brainstorm strategies for filling them on the next page. Go!

Key Group #1

1. _____
2. _____
3. _____
4. _____
5. _____
6. _____
7. _____
8. _____
9. _____
10. _____

Key Group #2

1. _____
2. _____
3. _____
4. _____
5. _____
6. _____
7. _____
8. _____
9. _____
10. _____

Key Group #3

1. _____
2. _____
3. _____
4. _____
5. _____
6. _____
7. _____
8. _____
9. _____
10. _____

Where to Focus My Efforts

Date _____ Current Rank _____ Current Volume $_____

Tasks

_____

_____

_____

_____

_____

_____

_____

_____

_____

_____

_____

_____

_____

_____

_____

_____

_____

_____

_____

_____

_____

_____

_____

_____

_____

_____

_____

_____

_____

WEEK FROM / TO /	MONDAY	TUESDAY	WEDNESDAY
THIS WEEK'S PRIORITIES	**TASKS**	**TASKS**	**TASKS**
1	1	1	1
2	2	2	2
3	3	3	3
4	4	4	4
5	5	5	5
6	6	6	6
7	7	7	7
8	8	8	8
	5:00	5:00	5:00
	5:30	5:30	5:30
	6:00	6:00	6:00
	6:30	6:30	6:30
	7:00	7:00	7:00
	7:30	7:30	7:30
	8:00	8:00	8:00
	8:30	8:30	8:30
	9:00	9:00	9:00
	9:30	9:30	9:30
	10:00	10:00	10:00
	10:30	10:30	10:30
	11:00	11:00	11:00
	11:30	11:30	11:30
	12:00p	12:00p	12:00p
	12:30	12:30	12:30
	1:00	1:00	1:00
	1:30	1:30	1:30
	2:00	2:00	2:00
	2:30	2:30	2:30
	3:00	3:00	3:00
	3:30	3:30	3:30
	4:00	4:00	4:00
	4:30	4:30	4:30
	5:00	5:00	5:00
	5:30	5:30	5:30
	6:00	6:00	6:00
	6:30	6:30	6:30
	7:00	7:00	7:00
	7:30	7:30	7:30
	8:00	8:00	8:00
	8:30	8:30	8:30
	9:00	9:00	9:00
	9:30	9:30	9:30
	10:00	10:00	10:00
	10:30	10:30	10:30

> Great things in business are never done by one person, they're done by a team of people.
> —Steve Jobs

TIME FOCUS KEY

1 = Your Miracle Morning
2 = Prospecting
3 = Presenting
4 = Following up
5 = Getting people started

TIME FOCUS:	1	2	3	4	5	1	2	3	4	5	1	2	3	4	5
✔ when completed:															

52

THURSDAY	FRIDAY	SATURDAY	SUNDAY
TASKS	**TASKS**	**TASKS**	**TASKS**
1	1	1	1
2	2	2	2
3	3	3	3
4	4	4	4
5	5	5	5
6	6	6	6
7	7	7	7
8	8	8	8
5:00	5:00	5:00	5:00
5:30	5:30	5:30	5:30
6:00	6:00	6:00	6:00
6:30	6:30	6:30	6:30
7:00	7:00	7:00	7:00
7:30	7:30	7:30	7:30
8:00	8:00	8:00	8:00
8:30	8:30	8:30	8:30
9:00	9:00	9:00	9:00
9:30	9:30	9:30	9:30
10:00	10:00	10:00	10:00
10:30	10:30	10:30	10:30
11:00	11:00	11:00	11:00
11:30	11:30	11:30	11:30
12:00p	12:00p	12:00p	12:00p
12:30	12:30	12:30	12:30
1:00	1:00	1:00	1:00
1:30	1:30	1:30	1:30
2:00	2:00	2:00	2:00
2:30	2:30	2:30	2:30
3:00	3:00	3:00	3:00
3:30	3:30	3:30	3:30
4:00	4:00	4:00	4:00
4:30	4:30	4:30	4:30
5:00	5:00	5:00	5:00
5:30	5:30	5:30	5:30
6:00	6:00	6:00	6:00
6:30	6:30	6:30	6:30
7:00	7:00	7:00	7:00
7:30	7:30	7:30	7:30
8:00	8:00	8:00	8:00
8:30	8:30	8:30	8:30
9:00	9:00	9:00	9:00
9:30	9:30	9:30	9:30
10:00	10:00	10:00	10:00
10:30	10:30	10:30	10:30

1	2	3	4	5	1	2	3	4	5	1	2	3	4	5	1	2	3	4	5
TASKS					**TASKS**					**TASKS**					**TASKS**				

Plan Your Work
Then Work Your Plan

Instructions

These clusters represent your 5 strongest groups. At the beginning of each week, fill in your current structure. Star the blanks that you want to work on filling this week. Brainstorm strategies for filling them on the next page. Go!

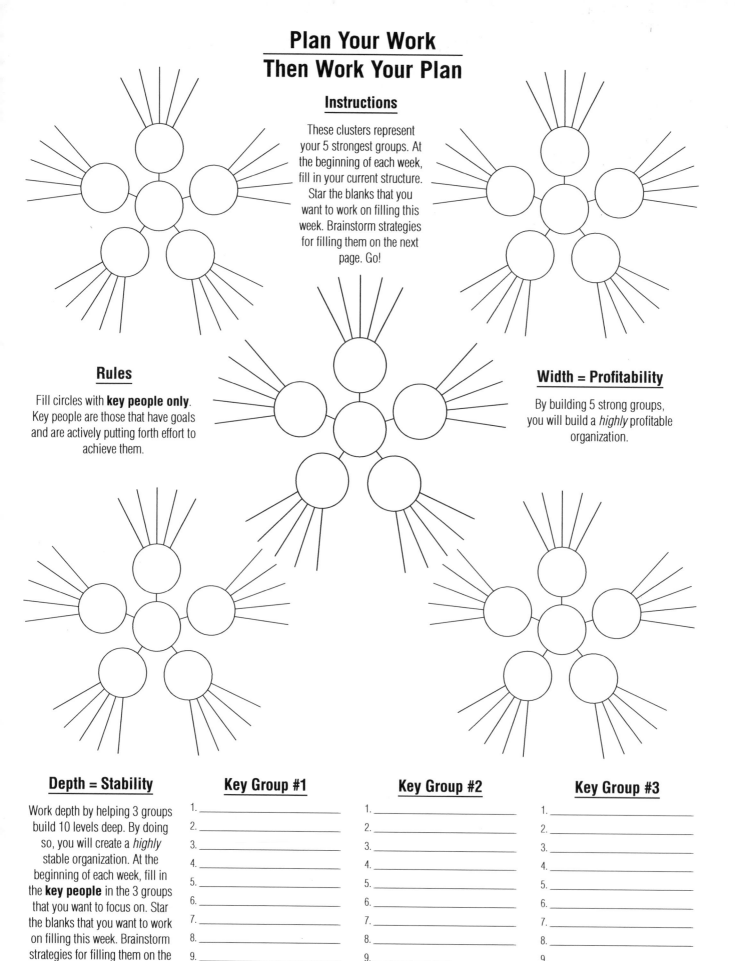

Rules

Fill circles with **key people only**. Key people are those that have goals and are actively putting forth effort to achieve them.

Width = Profitability

By building 5 strong groups, you will build a *highly* profitable organization.

Depth = Stability

Work depth by helping 3 groups build 10 levels deep. By doing so, you will create a *highly* stable organization. At the beginning of each week, fill in the **key people** in the 3 groups that you want to focus on. Star the blanks that you want to work on filling this week. Brainstorm strategies for filling them on the next page. Go!

Key Group #1

1. _____
2. _____
3. _____
4. _____
5. _____
6. _____
7. _____
8. _____
9. _____
10. _____

Key Group #2

1. _____
2. _____
3. _____
4. _____
5. _____
6. _____
7. _____
8. _____
9. _____
10. _____

Key Group #3

1. _____
2. _____
3. _____
4. _____
5. _____
6. _____
7. _____
8. _____
9. _____
10. _____

Where to Focus My Efforts

Date _____   Current Rank _____   Current Volume _$_____

Tasks

_____

_____

_____

_____

_____

_____

_____

_____

_____

_____

_____

_____

_____

_____

_____

_____

_____

_____

_____

_____

_____

_____

_____

_____

_____

_____

_____

_____

WEEK FROM / TO /	MONDAY		TUESDAY		WEDNESDAY	
THIS WEEK'S PRIORITIES	**TASKS**		**TASKS**		**TASKS**	
1	1		1		1	
2	2		2		2	
3	3		3		3	
4	4		4		4	
5	5		5		5	
6	6		6		6	
7	7		7		7	
8	8		8		8	
	5:00		5:00		5:00	
	5:30		5:30		5:30	
	6:00		6:00		6:00	
	6:30		6:30		6:30	
	7:00		7:00		7:00	
	7:30		7:30		7:30	
	8:00		8:00		8:00	
	8:30		8:30		8:30	
	9:00		9:00		9:00	
	9:30		9:30		9:30	
	10:00		10:00		10:00	
	10:30		10:30		10:30	
	11:00		11:00		11:00	
	11:30		11:30		11:30	
	12:00p		12:00p		12:00p	
	12:30		12:30		12:30	
	1:00		1:00		1:00	
	1:30		1:30		1:30	
	2:00		2:00		2:00	
	2:30		2:30		2:30	
	3:00		3:00		3:00	
	3:30		3:30		3:30	
	4:00		4:00		4:00	
	4:30		4:30		4:30	
	5:00		5:00		5:00	
	5:30		5:30		5:30	
	6:00		6:00		6:00	
	6:30		6:30		6:30	
	7:00		7:00		7:00	
	7:30		7:30		7:30	
	8:00		8:00		8:00	
	8:30		8:30		8:30	
	9:00		9:00		9:00	
	9:30		9:30		9:30	
	10:00		10:00		10:00	
	10:30		10:30		10:30	

Discipline is the bridge between goals and accomplishment.
—Jim Rohn

TIME FOCUS KEY
1 = Your Miracle Morning
2 = Prospecting
3 = Presenting
4 = Following up
5 = Getting people started

TIME FOCUS:	1	2	3	4	5	1	2	3	4	5	1	2	3	4	5
✔ when completed:															

THURSDAY		FRIDAY		SATURDAY		SUNDAY	
TASKS		TASKS		TASKS		TASKS	
1		1		1		1	
2		2		2		2	
3		3		3		3	
4		4		4		4	
5		5		5		5	
6		6		6		6	
7		7		7		7	
8		8		8		8	
5:00		5:00		5:00		5:00	
5:30		5:30		5:30		5:30	
6:00		6:00		6:00		6:00	
6:30		6:30		6:30		6:30	
7:00		7:00		7:00		7:00	
7:30		7:30		7:30		7:30	
8:00		8:00		8:00		8:00	
8:30		8:30		8:30		8:30	
9:00		9:00		9:00		9:00	
9:30		9:30		9:30		9:30	
10:00		10:00		10:00		10:00	
10:30		10:30		10:30		10:30	
11:00		11:00		11:00		11:00	
11:30		11:30		11:30		11:30	
12:00p		12:00p		12:00p		12:00p	
12:30		12:30		12:30		12:30	
1:00		1:00		1:00		1:00	
1:30		1:30		1:30		1:30	
2:00		2:00		2:00		2:00	
2:30		2:30		2:30		2:30	
3:00		3:00		3:00		3:00	
3:30		3:30		3:30		3:30	
4:00		4:00		4:00		4:00	
4:30		4:30		4:30		4:30	
5:00		5:00		5:00		5:00	
5:30		5:30		5:30		5:30	
6:00		6:00		6:00		6:00	
6:30		6:30		6:30		6:30	
7:00		7:00		7:00		7:00	
7:30		7:30		7:30		7:30	
8:00		8:00		8:00		8:00	
8:30		8:30		8:30		8:30	
9:00		9:00		9:00		9:00	
9:30		9:30		9:30		9:30	
10:00		10:00		10:00		10:00	
10:30		10:30		10:30		10:30	

1	2	3	4	5	1	2	3	4	5	1	2	3	4	5	1	2	3	4	5
TASKS					TASKS					TASKS					TASKS				

Plan Your Work
Then Work Your Plan

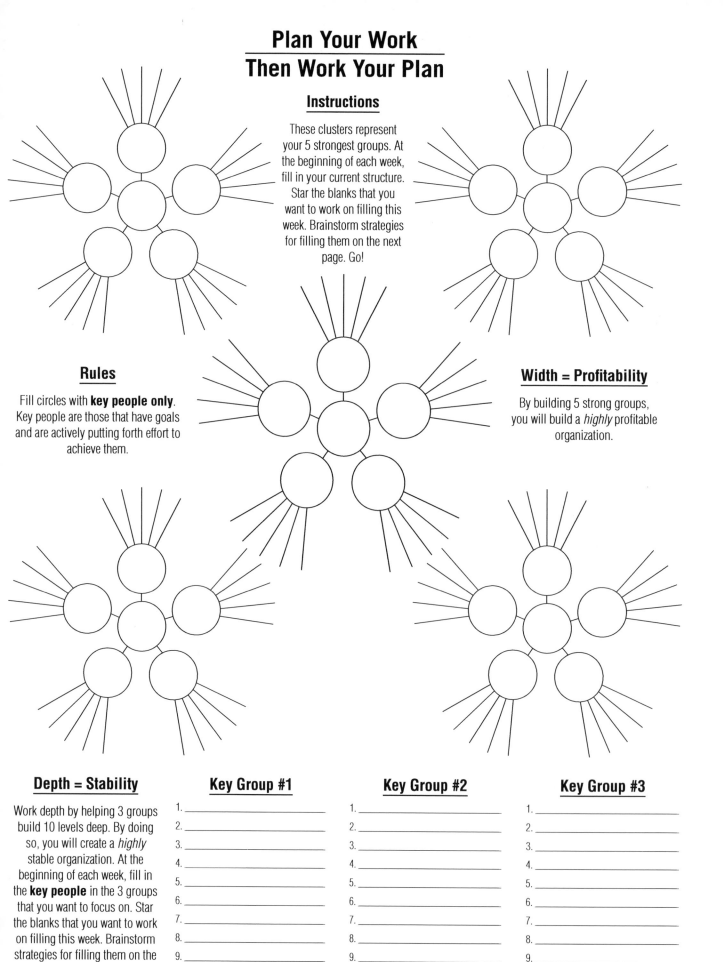

Instructions

These clusters represent your 5 strongest groups. At the beginning of each week, fill in your current structure. Star the blanks that you want to work on filling this week. Brainstorm strategies for filling them on the next page. Go!

Rules

Fill circles with **key people only**. Key people are those that have goals and are actively putting forth effort to achieve them.

Width = Profitability

By building 5 strong groups, you will build a *highly* profitable organization.

Depth = Stability

Work depth by helping 3 groups build 10 levels deep. By doing so, you will create a *highly* stable organization. At the beginning of each week, fill in the **key people** in the 3 groups that you want to focus on. Star the blanks that you want to work on filling this week. Brainstorm strategies for filling them on the next page. Go!

Key Group #1

1. _____
2. _____
3. _____
4. _____
5. _____
6. _____
7. _____
8. _____
9. _____
10. _____

Key Group #2

1. _____
2. _____
3. _____
4. _____
5. _____
6. _____
7. _____
8. _____
9. _____
10. _____

Key Group #3

1. _____
2. _____
3. _____
4. _____
5. _____
6. _____
7. _____
8. _____
9. _____
10. _____

Where to Focus My Efforts

Date _____ Current Rank _____ Current Volume $_____

Tasks

_____

_____

_____

_____

_____

_____

_____

_____

_____

_____

_____

_____

_____

_____

_____

_____

_____

_____

_____

_____

_____

_____

_____

_____

_____

_____

_____

_____

_____

_____

WEEK FROM ___/___ TO ___/___	MONDAY _____	TUESDAY _____	WEDNESDAY _____
THIS WEEK'S PRIORITIES	**TASKS**	**TASKS**	**TASKS**
1	1	1	1
2	2	2	2
3	3	3	3
4	4	4	4
5	5	5	5
6	6	6	6
7	7	7	7
8	8	8	8
	5:00	5:00	5:00
	5:30	5:30	5:30
	6:00	6:00	6:00
	6:30	6:30	6:30
	7:00	7:00	7:00
	7:30	7:30	7:30
	8:00	8:00	8:00
	8:30	8:30	8:30
	9:00	9:00	9:00
	9:30	9:30	9:30
	10:00	10:00	10:00
	10:30	10:30	10:30
	11:00	11:00	11:00
	11:30	11:30	11:30
	12:00p	12:00p	12:00p
	12:30	12:30	12:30
	1:00	1:00	1:00
	1:30	1:30	1:30
	2:00	2:00	2:00
	2:30	2:30	2:30
	3:00	3:00	3:00
	3:30	3:30	3:30
	4:00	4:00	4:00
	4:30	4:30	4:30
	5:00	5:00	5:00
	5:30	5:30	5:30
	6:00	6:00	6:00
	6:30	6:30	6:30
	7:00	7:00	7:00
	7:30	7:30	7:30
	8:00	8:00	8:00
	8:30	8:30	8:30
	9:00	9:00	9:00
	9:30	9:30	9:30
	10:00	10:00	10:00
	10:30	10:30	10:30

When you come to the boundaries of what you know, it is time to make some mistakes.
—Robert Kiyosaki

TIME FOCUS KEY
1 = Your Miracle Morning
2 = Prospecting
3 = Presenting
4 = Following up
5 = Getting people started

TIME FOCUS:	1	2	3	4	5	1	2	3	4	5	1	2	3	4	5
✔ when completed:															

THURSDAY	FRIDAY	SATURDAY	SUNDAY
TASKS	TASKS	TASKS	TASKS
1	1	1	1
2	2	2	2
3	3	3	3
4	4	4	4
5	5	5	5
6	6	6	6
7	7	7	7
8	8	8	8
5:00	5:00	5:00	5:00
5:30	5:30	5:30	5:30
6:00	6:00	6:00	6:00
6:30	6:30	6:30	6:30
7:00	7:00	7:00	7:00
7:30	7:30	7:30	7:30
8:00	8:00	8:00	8:00
8:30	8:30	8:30	8:30
9:00	9:00	9:00	9:00
9:30	9:30	9:30	9:30
10:00	10:00	10:00	10:00
10:30	10:30	10:30	10:30
11:00	11:00	11:00	11:00
11:30	11:30	11:30	11:30
12:00p	12:00p	12:00p	12:00p
12:30	12:30	12:30	12:30
1:00	1:00	1:00	1:00
1:30	1:30	1:30	1:30
2:00	2:00	2:00	2:00
2:30	2:30	2:30	2:30
3:00	3:00	3:00	3:00
3:30	3:30	3:30	3:30
4:00	4:00	4:00	4:00
4:30	4:30	4:30	4:30
5:00	5:00	5:00	5:00
5:30	5:30	5:30	5:30
6:00	6:00	6:00	6:00
6:30	6:30	6:30	6:30
7:00	7:00	7:00	7:00
7:30	7:30	7:30	7:30
8:00	8:00	8:00	8:00
8:30	8:30	8:30	8:30
9:00	9:00	9:00	9:00
9:30	9:30	9:30	9:30
10:00	10:00	10:00	10:00
10:30	10:30	10:30	10:30

1	2	3	4	5	1	2	3	4	5	1	2	3	4	5	1	2	3	4	5
TASKS					TASKS					TASKS					TASKS				

Plan Your Work
Then Work Your Plan

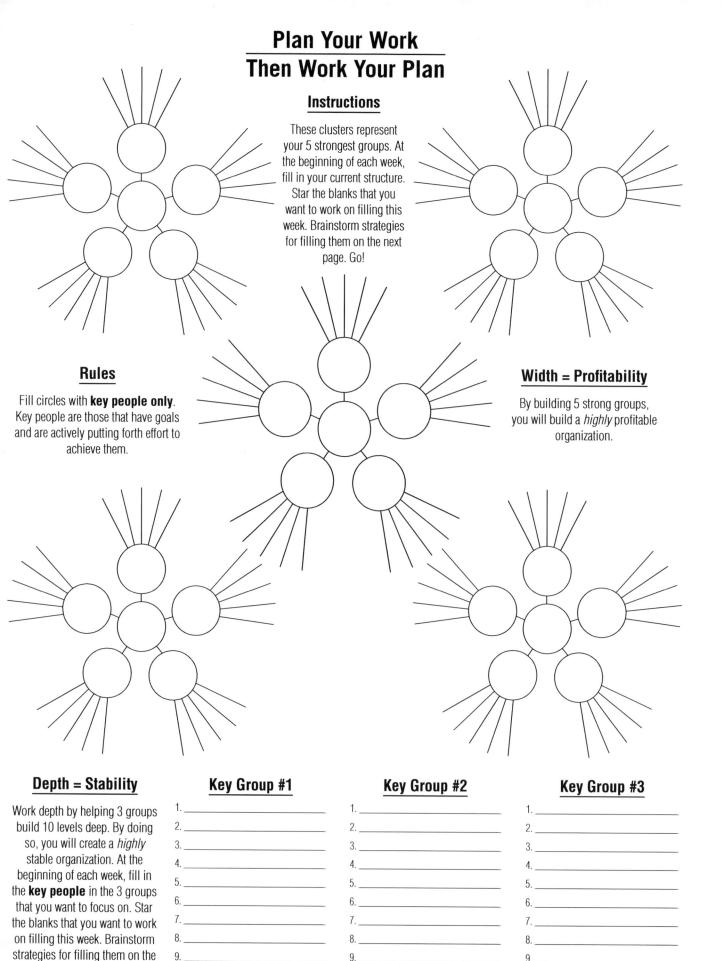

Instructions

These clusters represent your 5 strongest groups. At the beginning of each week, fill in your current structure. Star the blanks that you want to work on filling this week. Brainstorm strategies for filling them on the next page. Go!

Rules

Fill circles with **key people only**. Key people are those that have goals and are actively putting forth effort to achieve them.

Width = Profitability

By building 5 strong groups, you will build a *highly* profitable organization.

Depth = Stability

Work depth by helping 3 groups build 10 levels deep. By doing so, you will create a *highly* stable organization. At the beginning of each week, fill in the **key people** in the 3 groups that you want to focus on. Star the blanks that you want to work on filling this week. Brainstorm strategies for filling them on the next page. Go!

Key Group #1

1. _____
2. _____
3. _____
4. _____
5. _____
6. _____
7. _____
8. _____
9. _____
10. _____

Key Group #2

1. _____
2. _____
3. _____
4. _____
5. _____
6. _____
7. _____
8. _____
9. _____
10. _____

Key Group #3

1. _____
2. _____
3. _____
4. _____
5. _____
6. _____
7. _____
8. _____
9. _____
10. _____

Where to Focus My Efforts

Date _____ Current Rank _____ Current Volume $ _____

Tasks

_____

_____

_____

_____

_____

_____

_____

_____

_____

_____

_____

_____

_____

_____

_____

_____

_____

_____

_____

_____

_____

_____

_____

_____

_____

_____

_____

WEEK FROM	/ TO /	MONDAY		TUESDAY		WEDNESDAY	
THIS WEEK'S PRIORITIES		TASKS		TASKS		TASKS	
1		1		1		1	
2		2		2		2	
3		3		3		3	
4		4		4		4	
5		5		5		5	
6		6		6		6	
7		7		7		7	
8		8		8		8	
		5:00		5:00		5:00	
		5:30		5:30		5:30	
		6:00		6:00		6:00	
		6:30		6:30		6:30	
		7:00		7:00		7:00	
		7:30		7:30		7:30	
		8:00		8:00		8:00	
		8:30		8:30		8:30	
		9:00		9:00		9:00	
		9:30		9:30		9:30	
		10:00		10:00		10:00	
		10:30		10:30		10:30	
		11:00		11:00		11:00	
		11:30		11:30		11:30	
		12:00p		12:00p		12:00p	
		12:30		12:30		12:30	
		1:00		1:00		1:00	
		1:30		1:30		1:30	
		2:00		2:00		2:00	
		2:30		2:30		2:30	
		3:00		3:00		3:00	
		3:30		3:30		3:30	
		4:00		4:00		4:00	
		4:30		4:30		4:30	
		5:00		5:00		5:00	
		5:30		5:30		5:30	
		6:00		6:00		6:00	
		6:30		6:30		6:30	
		7:00		7:00		7:00	
		7:30		7:30		7:30	
		8:00		8:00		8:00	
		8:30		8:30		8:30	
		9:00		9:00		9:00	
		9:30		9:30		9:30	
		10:00		10:00		10:00	
		10:30		10:30		10:30	

Losers quit when they fail. Winners fail until they succeed.
—Robert Kiyosaki

TIME FOCUS KEY
1 = Your Miracle Morning
2 = Prospecting
3 = Presenting
4 = Following up
5 = Getting people started

TIME FOCUS:	1	2	3	4	5	1	2	3	4	5	1	2	3	4	5
✔ when completed:															
		TASKS			TASKS			TASKS		

THURSDAY		FRIDAY		SATURDAY		SUNDAY	
TASKS		**TASKS**		**TASKS**		**TASKS**	
1		1		1		1	
2		2		2		2	
3		3		3		3	
4		4		4		4	
5		5		5		5	
6		6		6		6	
7		7		7		7	
8		8		8		8	
5:00		5:00		5:00		5:00	
5:30		5:30		5:30		5:30	
6:00		6:00		6:00		6:00	
6:30		6:30		6:30		6:30	
7:00		7:00		7:00		7:00	
7:30		7:30		7:30		7:30	
8:00		8:00		8:00		8:00	
8:30		8:30		8:30		8:30	
9:00		9:00		9:00		9:00	
9:30		9:30		9:30		9:30	
10:00		10:00		10:00		10:00	
10:30		10:30		10:30		10:30	
11:00		11:00		11:00		11:00	
11:30		11:30		11:30		11:30	
12:00p		12:00p		12:00p		12:00p	
12:30		12:30		12:30		12:30	
1:00		1:00		1:00		1:00	
1:30		1:30		1:30		1:30	
2:00		2:00		2:00		2:00	
2:30		2:30		2:30		2:30	
3:00		3:00		3:00		3:00	
3:30		3:30		3:30		3:30	
4:00		4:00		4:00		4:00	
4:30		4:30		4:30		4:30	
5:00		5:00		5:00		5:00	
5:30		5:30		5:30		5:30	
6:00		6:00		6:00		6:00	
6:30		6:30		6:30		6:30	
7:00		7:00		7:00		7:00	
7:30		7:30		7:30		7:30	
8:00		8:00		8:00		8:00	
8:30		8:30		8:30		8:30	
9:00		9:00		9:00		9:00	
9:30		9:30		9:30		9:30	
10:00		10:00		10:00		10:00	
10:30		10:30		10:30		10:30	

1	2	3	4	5	1	2	3	4	5	1	2	3	4	5	1	2	3	4	5
TASKS					**TASKS**					**TASKS**					**TASKS**				

Master List

Name	Phone	Email	Followup Date	Source	Rating	State

Master List

Name	Phone	Email	Followup Date	Source	Rating	State

Master List

Name	Phone	Email	Followup Date	Source	Rating	State

Master List

Name	Phone	Email	Followup Date	Source	Rating	State

Master List

Name	Phone	Email	Followup Date	Source	Rating	State

Master List

Name	Phone	Email	Followup Date	Source	Rating	State

Master List

Name	Phone	Email	Followup Date	Source	Rating	State

Master List

Name	Phone	Email	Followup Date	Source	Rating	State

Active List

Name	Phone	Email	Followup Date	Source	Rating	State

Active List

Name	Phone	Email	Followup Date	Source	Rating	State

Active List

Name	Phone	Email	Followup Date	Source	Rating	State

Active List

Name	Phone	Email	Followup Date	Source	Rating	State

Drip List

Name	Phone	Email	Followup Date	Source	Rating	State

Drip List

Name	Phone	Email	Followup Date	Source	Rating	State

Drip List

Name	Phone	Email	Followup Date	Source	Rating	State

Drip List

Name	Phone	Email	Followup Date	Source	Rating	State

Notes

Notes

Notes

NOTES

Notes

Notes

NOTES

Notes

Notes

Notes

Notes

NOTES

Notes

Notes

NOTES

Notes

Notes

Notes

Notes

NOTES

Notes

Notes

NOTES

Notes

Notes

NOTES

Notes

Notes

NOTES

Notes

Notes

104

NOTES

Notes

Do a 90-Day Review

Celebrate!
What went well?

_____

_____

_____

_____

_____

Evaluate
What didn't?

_____

_____

_____

_____

Plan
What do I need to do better next time?

_____

_____

_____

_____

_____

Plan Your Next Blitz

1. Order your new planner.
2. Order a 10 (100!) pack for your team.
3. Schedule your dates.
4. Schedule your kick-off call.
5. Go!

Check Out Our Bulk Discounts at

www.TMMforNetworkMarketers.com/order

For questions, contact us at
support@TMMforNetworkMarketers.com

CONGRATS

90-day blitz. done. ✓

Made in the USA
San Bernardino, CA
12 March 2017